The Twelve Steps

&

Twelve Traditions

Workbook

of

Co-Dependents Anonymous

Co-Dependents Anonymous, Inc.
P.O. Box 33577
Phoenix, AZ 85067-3577
USA
602-277-7991
Toll Free: 888-444-2359
Spanish Toll Free: 888-444-2379
www.coda.org

Third Consolidated Edition: January 2013
First Printing

For additional copies of this workbook, or to order other
CoDA Conference endorsed literature, contact:

CoRe Publications
P.O. Box 1004
Denver, NC 28037-1004
USA
Phone: 704-483-3038
Fax: 704-483-3088
Email: coreorders@coda.org
Online ordering: www.coda.org/estore

Dear CoDA Member,

The Twelve Steps & Twelve Traditions Workbook is the result of a long and rewarding group conscience process.

This project started when a group of CoDA members began to meet weekly to discuss a Step and the corresponding Tradition. After they wrote about their discussions, the material was sent to the CoDA Literature Committee (CLC) for editing and rewriting. The CLC submitted the edited versions to the CoDA Service Conference for endorsement. It was then printed and distributed to the Fellowship.

We who have participated in this project have experienced great recovery through the group conscience process. We are grateful for the opportunity to have served the Fellowship of Co-Dependents Anonymous.

In Service,

CoDA's Literature Committee

Table of Contents

Preface

As the material for our study group was prepared, it became evident that there are three areas covered in the Steps. They are:

- Identifying our codependent characteristics and their manifestations in our lives—OUR EXPERIENCE.

- Using the tools in our program—OUR STRENGTH.

- The rewards of using these tools and experiencing recovery—OUR HOPE.

We found the Traditions offer us guidelines as we work our recovery, do our service work, and live our program.

Throughout this Workbook you will find codependency referred to as a disease. Many in our group found this quite helpful, and perhaps even necessary, in terms of understanding the effects of codependency, identifying when codependent symptoms appear, and learning to apply the tools of our program (self-care) as we recover, much as we might do in recovery from any other disease. This thought also brings, for many of us, a continuing sense of acceptance about our codependency as we walk our path of recovery. As one person in our group shared, "When I heard others refer to what I had as a disease, it released me from being responsible for my codependency. I could feel free of shame and blame and move on."

Webster's dictionary defines the word disease as "a condition of the living animal or plant body or of one of its parts that impairs the performance of a vital function; sickness; malady; trouble; a harmful development." It is in the spirit of this definition that our group conscience voted to use this word as a description of codependency.

Our group's study of the Traditions made it evident that they offer essential guidelines for our service work and for living our program. We acknowledged our need to be steadfast in our allegiance to the Traditions. We believe the Traditions are to the group what the Steps are to the individual. Our understanding of the interrelations of the Steps and Traditions deepened. We saw that the awareness gained in our Step work can be used in our application of the Traditions in our service work, our meetings, and with one another. We can learn to live our recovery in service and to focus on CoDA as a whole.

As codependents, we acknowledge that we are people unskilled in managing our own lives and relationships. Whatever our issues, we find hope through a common solution: The Twelve Steps and Twelve Traditions. It is not necessary for us to understand how or why the Steps and Traditions work, but rather to trust that they do. This trust is not misplaced; we see those among us realizing the Promises of the program. We have faith that the spiritual principles found in our Steps and Traditions support our recovery and our Fellowship.

The Twelve Steps of Co-Dependents Anonymous* ©

1. We admitted we were powerless over others–that our lives had become unmanageable.

2. Came to believe that a power greater than ourselves could restore us to sanity.

3. Made a decision to turn our will and our lives over to the care of God as we understood God.

4. Made a searching and fearless moral inventory of ourselves.

5. Admitted to God, to ourselves, and to another human being the exact nature of our wrongs.

6. Were entirely ready to have God remove all these defects of character.

7. Humbly asked God to remove our shortcomings.

8. Made a list of all persons we had harmed, and became willing to make amends to them all.

9. Made direct amends to such people wherever possible, except when to do so would injure them or others.

10. Continued to take personal inventory and when we were wrong promptly admitted it.

11. Sought through prayer and meditation to improve our conscious contact with God as we understood God, praying only for knowledge of God's will for us and the power to carry that out.

12. Having had a spiritual awakening as the result of these steps, we tried to carry this message to other codependents, and to practice these principles in all our affairs.

The Twelve Traditions of Co-Dependents Anonymous* ©

1. Our common welfare should come first; personal recovery depends upon CoDA unity.

2. For our group purpose there is but one ultimate authority—a loving Higher Power as expressed to our group conscience. Our leaders are but trusted servants; they do not govern.

3. The only requirement for membership in CoDA is a desire for healthy and loving relationships.

4. Each group should remain autonomous except in matters affecting other groups or CoDA as a whole.

5. Each group has but one primary purpose—to carry its message to other codependents who still suffer.

6. A CoDA group ought never endorse, finance, or lend the CoDA name to any related facility or outside enterprise, lest problems of money, property, and prestige divert us from our primary spiritual aim.

7. Every CoDA group ought to be fully self-supporting, declining outside contributions.

8. Co-Dependents Anonymous should remain forever nonprofessional, but our service centers may employ special workers.

9. CoDA, as such, ought never be organized; but we may create service boards or committees directly responsible to those they serve.

10. CoDA has no opinion on outside issues; hence, the CoDA name ought never be drawn into public controversy.

11. Our public relations policy is based on attraction rather than promotion; we need always maintain personal anonymity at the level of press, radio, and films.

12. Anonymity is the spiritual foundation of all our traditions, ever reminding us to place principles before personalities.

The Twelve Promises of Co-Dependents Anonymous ©

I can expect a miraculous change in my life by working the program of Co-Dependents Anonymous. As I make an honest effort to work the Twelve Steps and follow the Twelve Traditions....

1. I know a new sense of belonging. The feelings of emptiness and loneliness will disappear.

2. I am no longer controlled by my fears. I overcome my fears and act with courage, integrity, and dignity.

3. I know a new freedom.

4. I release myself from worry, guilt, and regret about my past and present. I am aware enough not to repeat it.

5. I know a new love and acceptance of myself and others. I feel genuinely lovable, loving, and loved.

6. I learn to see myself as equal to others. My new and renewed relationships are all with equal partners.

7. I am capable of developing and maintaining healthy and loving relationships. The need to control and manipulate others will disappear as I learn to trust those who are trustworthy.

8. I learn that it is possible for me to mend—to become more loving, intimate, and supportive. I have the choice of communicating with my family in a way which is safe for me and respectful of them.

9. I acknowledge that I am a unique and precious creation.

10. I no longer need to rely solely on others to provide my sense of worth.

11. I trust the guidance I receive from my Higher Power and come to believe in my own capabilities.

12. I gradually experience serenity, strength, and spiritual growth in my daily life.

We admitted we were powerless over others—
that our lives had become unmanageable.

—Step One

Step One begins our personal relationship with the Steps of Co-Dependents Anonymous. We admit we are powerless over our disease of codependency to ourselves and to others. As we do this, many of us begin to experience a sense of belonging and we see that we are not alone. Even though new behavior may feel uncomfortable, we can address each situation in our lives one at a time with the Steps, beginning with Step One. We can stop trying to control; we begin to establish a new relationship with ourselves.

Saying we are powerless over our disease, out loud to the group, starts us on our road of truth. We begin to identify what we are powerless over and see the manifestations of our disease. We learn to identify some of the "untruths" we may have been taught. We come to realize that powerless does not mean weak; controlling others does not make us safe; looking to others for our direction does not support us in living our own lives; judging others is not our business; and believing we are all-powerful is painful. We experience how old tapes playing in our heads can control us. We discover that thinking in terms of black and white or right and wrong is rigid and limiting.

As we work Step One, we begin to find the tools of recovery. Most of us find that using our CoDA literature, as well as listening to others as they share their codependent characteristics, is helpful in the identification process required in Step One. We focus on ourselves and work on staying in the present. We begin to recognize a Higher Power. As we let go, we begin to release responsibility for others. We let go of what others think about us, knowing we are adults and have choices. We learn to ask, "What do I want?," "What do I think?," and "What do I feel?" We can make a checklist of tools to support our recovery. We can be still and connect with a Higher Power. We begin to establish healthy boundaries (leave, call someone, take a walk around the block) to better take care of ourselves. We learn that we have done enough when we have listened to our gut, prayed, written, or realized we don't have to make a decision right away. We also learn that it isn't necessary to like everything that we accept. We can learn the lessons of true humility and recognize we don't have all the answers. As we begin to let go of control, we are better able to accept the realities of being human. We find peace.

Our lives are different and rewarding when we are willing to work this Step. We experience freedom, personal integrity, and self-empowerment. Developing a genuine interest in taking care of ourselves and honoring our intuition becomes a priority. As we let go of the need to control others, we begin to focus on that which we can take care of: OURSELVES. We can take our time and act with grace and dignity. When we are connected with ourselves and this Step, we begin to have faith that we are capable of changing, and we learn to release our fears. We begin to recognize we are worthwhile and valuable. We can say "thank you" and give ourselves positive affirmations daily.

Robert
Therman

9

We admitted we were powerless over others—
that our lives had become unmanageable.

—Step One

These questions are intended to help you work Step One:

• Am I controlling? How?

• What is the difference between being powerless and being empowered?

• When I let go of others, how am I then empowered? How does this make my life manageable?

• How do I let go of the fear of what others think? How do I take care of myself? How does my acceptance of being "powerless over others" assist me in this task?

• Which codependent characteristics (character defects) keep me from taking Step One?

• Why does this Step say "admitted we were powerless" instead of admitted I was powerless?

• What do powerlessness and unmanageability mean to me today?

• What signs do I see that indicate I'm in denial?

• What does surrender mean? Why do I need to surrender? Over what do I need to surrender?

• When do I know I've done enough?

• What are signs of my unmanageability? (Make a list)

• Why do I want to control? *my reactiveness,*

• Am I willing to realize that trying to change anyone brings on unmanageability, hostility, resentment?

• Am I powerless over my codependent behavior?

10

NOTES

At times I'm controlling, mainly at work.

I think being powerless over situations I have no controll over, recognizing this is important and knowing the difference and not trying to impose myself on others allows others to be themselves and empowers me.

— I feel free when I'm not concerning myself w/ what others do, think but just being me and living life

I have trouble letting go of what some people think mainly my Dgt & girlfriend

11

NOTES

NOTES

NOTES

Our common welfare should come first;
personal recovery depends upon CoDA unity.

—Tradition One

Beginning with Tradition One, we practice new behaviors and follow new guidelines in order to restructure our lives in recovery. We become willing to let go of our own egos and personal agendas in order to support the common welfare of CoDA. We learn to speak our truth and we allow others the same privilege. We honor the group conscience process by acknowledging our Higher Power. We let go of our need to control the outcome and accept the results of the group conscience.

Tradition One supports us in all aspects of our service work whether this be at an individual, group, regional, national, or international level. It helps us create a functional environment wherein we can attend to the business of Co-Dependents Anonymous. We also find that keeping the spirit of Tradition One in our minds and hearts is essential to working with others. Having acknowledged our difficulties in forming and maintaining functional relationships, we look to Tradition One: our common welfare should come first and our personal recovery depends upon our unity.

As we do our service work, our Step One issues may surface. We find ourselves wanting to control and may actively attempt to manipulate people, places, and things according to our rigid ideas of how they should be. We may want to be the Higher Power or believe we must have the right answers. We may look to others to be our Higher Power and provide answers for us. We can become overly attached to our own opinions or see our differences with others as attacks or threats. Again, we need to place the focus back where it belongs—our common welfare, upon which the unity of our program is dependent. By actively applying the principles of our program, we see that neither control nor compliance supports our common welfare and unity. We learn to listen, to open our minds and our hearts, and to make room for a Higher Power. We seek serenity within ourselves.

Tradition One allows us the opportunity to restructure our lives outside the meeting rooms of Co-Dependents Anonymous. Tradition One serves as a guideline as we learn to practice recovery in our daily lives. Again, we make room for a Higher Power and loosen our tight grasp of how we believe things should be. We learn to care for ourselves by identifying and expressing our feelings, needs, and boundaries. We allow others to do the same. Caring about our own needs is healthy. Allowing others to care for their needs supports the structure of a safe and loving environment. The idea of common welfare and unity being primary can be brought into our recovery in CoDA, as well as with our families and other relationships.

With our deepening awareness of Tradition One, we begin to truly understand how essential the unity of the program is to our personal recovery. Without a strong spiritual structure, most of us believe that, over time, Co-Dependents Anonymous would cease to exist. Therefore, without consistent practice of this Tradition, there would be no place for our recovery. Even the simple process of saying in a meeting "I am Jane, and I am codependent" and having our name repeated, promotes our common welfare. We identify as codependents and acknowledge there is a place for each and every one of us in our program. This process allows for acceptance by helping us remember that no one is more important than another, and we all share a common trait: our codependence.

Our common welfare should come first;
personal recovery depends upon CoDA unity.

—Tradition One

These questions are intended to help you work Tradition One:

- Why is CoDA unity important to my personal recovery?

- When placing CoDA's welfare first, do I give up anything?

- How does honoring the Twelve Steps and Twelve Traditions
  (common welfare and unity) create a place for my personal recovery?

- What does CoDA unity mean?

- What is our common welfare?

- How can Tradition One support me in all of my relationships?

- How does my surrounding environment support me in functional living?

- How do I value myself appropriately and yet have our common welfare come first?

- What tools can I use to remember that others are entitled to their opinions?

- What does this phrase mean? "I can't keep it, unless I give it away."
  How does it apply to Tradition One?

NOTES

NOTES

NOTES

NOTES

Came to believe that a power greater than ourselves
could restore us to sanity.

—Step Two

Having admitted our powerlessness in Step One, Step Two asks us to trust. We acknowledge our need to believe in, and rely on, something greater than ourselves. For many of us, this is the first time we are able to recognize that we are not the center of the universe. There is a plan and a power greater than anything we could possibly imagine on our own. We may now recognize the painful consequences of allowing others to be this power for us. We can experience humility, and relieve ourselves of grandiosity and our obsession to control. We are not the "power greater than ourselves," nor can others be this power for us. We begin to see how these patterns of thinking and behaving created unmanageability in our lives. Believing in a power greater than ourselves can restore us to sanity—if we are willing.

As children, our parents and/or others were that power greater than ourselves. If these experiences left us unable to trust, we may now find it difficult to rely on anything or anyone, even ourselves. We may have learned that this power greater than ourselves was punishing, mean, unforgiving, or unavailable. We may also believe that we are unworthy of love and guidance. As we seek help, letting go of control can often be a terrifying prospect.

At this point, we can remember that the program allows us complete freedom to define this power for ourselves. Some of us find our definition of, and relationship with, a Higher Power changes over time. Each of us can begin with whatever belief provides the most comfort, using whatever degree of faith we have at the moment. For some, a Higher Power is the harmony of the universe or the power of meetings. For others, it can be God, love, nature, or, for one member— even an old shoe. Some of us place our faith in those who have come before us, believing because they believe. Our definitions matter less than our willingness to work Step Two. Yet our group experience shows us it is important to trust that this power cares for us, has our best interests at heart, and can offer us the guidance we seek.

Step Two is a daily part of our program of recovery. The words "came to believe" remind us that this is a process. Our faith and serenity grow and deepen through our willingness to trust this process. We practice using the tools of our program; and we act upon our desire to believe by going to meetings, listening to others, feeling our feelings, finding a sponsor, praying, and meditating. As we practice letting go, we can relax and remember that we are not in charge and we can ask for guidance from this Higher Power. By working Step Two, we come to believe that this power greater than ourselves can restore us to sanity.

Came to believe that a power greater than ourselves could restore us to sanity.

—Step Two

These questions are intended to help you work Step Two:

- Do I need to believe in any power other than my own?

- What, if anything, prevents me from believing in a power greater than myself?

- How can I find my Higher Power?

- What attributes does my Higher Power have? How do they support me?

- What does "came to believe" mean to me?

- What does a "power greater than ourselves" mean to me?

- What does "restore us to sanity" mean to me?

- For today, what does sanity mean to me?

- What was my image of a Higher Power before I came to CoDA?

- How did my grandiosity and obsessive controlling manifest themselves in my life?

- As a result of working Step Two, what new behaviors am I practicing? In what ways am I still suffering?

NOTES

NOTES

NOTES

NOTES

For our group purpose there is but one ultimate authority—
a loving Higher Power as expressed to our group conscience.
Our leaders are but trusted servants; they do not govern.

—Tradition Two

Tradition Two reminds us that a loving Higher Power is greater than the individual, group, or trusted servant. This Tradition allows us to experience humility by recognizing where our direction comes from. This Tradition points out that no one person leads the group, makes plans for the group, or provides answers for the group. The group conscience process offers us safety. Without crosstalk, arguing or shaming, we become willing to speak our truth, remain open to others' opinions, and let go of results. We listen to what is being said, instead of noticing who is saying it. Knowing we can take care of ourselves, we can experience our feelings of vulnerability. We are afforded the opportunity to say we have changed our minds. We can also release black and white thinking, such as: "If I am right, you are wrong," or "I must have all the answers." Knowing that group members can only speak from their place in recovery, we strive to avoid judging one another. We believe in progress, not perfection. We honor the outcome of the group conscience.

We accept the group conscience as our ultimate authority. Tradition Two allows for all concepts of Higher Power to share the room. We begin to experience humility in our lives. We let go of the urge to take on more than we can handle. As trusted servants, we do not create direction— we receive direction from the Fellowship. We let go of our own agenda, trust the group conscience, and remember that we don't have to like something we accept.

Apart from understanding what it means to be a trusted servant, Tradition Two begins to define the structure of our program:

- a loving Higher Power
- the group conscience
- trusted servants

The structure of Tradition Two provides unity and, with unity, we can recover.

In old thinking, we had to have the answers right away, sometimes even before the questions were asked. Today, as we work our program, we learn to choose our response instead of reacting immediately. Ideally, issues brought to our local, regional, national, or international levels come to a vote after having gone through the group conscience process at each respective level. As trusted servants, we find it helpful to wait for a period of time after a motion is presented. This allows members time for meditation and conscious contact with Higher Power before reaching a group conscience decision. There are very few issues that require an immediate decision. At each level, a discussion is held so that all members have an opportunity to speak their individual or group opinion. This allows Higher Power to work at each level of the Fellowship.

For our group purpose there is but one ultimate authority—
a loving Higher Power as expressed to our group conscience.
Our leaders are but trusted servants; they do not govern.
—Tradition Two

These questions are intended to help you work Tradition Two:

- In light of Tradition Two, what does a "loving Higher Power" mean to me today?

- How does the group conscience begin to establish CoDA structure?

- How does Tradition Two help me to accept the group conscience?

- How do I learn to trust my Higher Power?

- How does my Higher Power help me to trust myself?

- How does Tradition Two relate to Step Two?

- What does "our leaders are but trusted servants" mean to me? Is being a trusted servant and being a leader mutually exclusive?

- How does being a trusted servant relate to my recovery?

- How can humility bring me serenity?

- Why is the word "loving" so important in the application of Tradition Two?

- How well does my group apply Tradition Two?

NOTES

NOTES

NOTES

NOTES

Made a decision to turn our will and our lives
over to the care of God as we understood God.

—Step Three

Step Three offers us the opportunity to make a decision and to have faith in a power greater than ourselves. Many of us begin working this Step with small things, such as making a decision not to fix someone, letting our feelings just be there, or not trying to control, just for a few minutes at a time. As we experience the benefits of working Step Three, we find ourselves more willing to trust in the care of a loving Higher Power and to experience faith.

The primary purpose of this Step is to begin living our lives in a new way. Finally, we have a tool that works and provides us the freedom and acceptance we were incapable of finding through self-will alone. This Step suggests a willingness to live in this decision. We surrender ourselves to a Higher Power of our own understanding. When we do this, we can begin new, more satisfying relationships with ourselves and others. As we develop the courage and willingness required in Step Three, many of us come to acknowledge and believe that we are part of God's plan, and we become increasingly capable of knowing ourselves as God—and not others—intended us to be.

As codependents, our gods have often been other powerful forces. We may have been ruled by fear, anger, resentment, guilt, and a powerful urge to take care of, or be taken care of, by those we have invested with "authority" to govern our lives. In Step Three, we can begin to let go of these powerful forces which have controlled us and align ourselves, our thinking, and our actions with our Higher Power.

Letting go can be seen as a decision to trust in a Higher Power. Letting God can be seen as living in this power's will and doing our best to take whatever actions are necessary to take care of ourselves today, without attempting to control results tomorrow. It can be frightening to trust in something we cannot see and to have faith that all is happening on schedule, especially when we may have been unable to trust our parents or other authority figures throughout our childhood years. However, most of us find this struggle to trust well worth our efforts. We can accept our fear, ask our Higher Power's guidance, and practice faith. In this way, we give ourselves permission to begin and to start expanding whatever amount of belief we have.

Some of us believed that making a decision to "turn our will and our lives over to the care of God" meant that we needed to give up our selves: what we thought, wanted, and felt. Indeed, for many years, we often did lose our sense of self and autonomy. Our fear of this may cause great resistance. Many of us find comfort in those who have walked before us, when we see and hear how this Step transformed them into the people they were meant to be.

We can allow ourselves to be cradled in care and in faith. We can learn to be in the present moment and live God's will for us. We can let go of trying to control and making things OK for ourselves and others in ways that no longer work for, or protect, us. We can find courage in a Higher Power: the ability to be who and what we are. We can develop faith in ourselves with the help of a Higher Power and we can learn to understand that our answers are only for ourselves.

Feeling a sense of urgency, feeling that we have to do something different, or feeling resentment, can all be signals that we need to let go and work Step Three. Positive affirmations support us in learning new behavior. Using these affirmations to replace the old tapes in our heads can open us to our Higher Power's will. Learning new behavior takes time. We can give ourselves permission to be human!

When we let go, miracles happen. We begin to feel the rewards of the program and of this Step. The more we trust in this process, the more we are able to let go. We learn to practice patience and acceptance. Our lives translate into results when we accept Step One, have faith with Step Two guiding us, and let go with Step Three. We make the "decision to turn our will and our lives over to the care of" our Higher Power, as we understand this Higher Power, again and again. Constant vigilance in our program appears to be essential for codependents. As such, many of us find great freedom in the daily action, practice, and renewal of Step Three.

Tools

Following are some tools available to us in working Step Three. These tools have been freely offered by members of CoDA in the spirit of light, love, and the hope of recovery.

- Acknowledge that we are codependent and need the help of our Higher Power in order to recover fully.

- Let go so that our Higher Power can work in our lives.

- Be still, accept our feelings, and not have to do something to make the feelings go away.

- Ask our Higher Power for help, recognize that we do not have to do it alone.

- Make a phone call to our sponsor or to other people in recovery.

- Go back to Step One (admit we are powerless), move into Step Two (acknowledge our belief in a Higher Power), and work Step Three (accept that our Higher Power has a plan for us greater than any we could imagine, and let go).

- Use the *Serenity Prayer* or other favorite prayer or meditation to reconnect to our program.

- Remind ourselves of previous situations in which we let go, and later discovered that things worked out well.

- Reflect on the fact that we may not understand God.

- Repeat the affirmation "I am capable of changing."

- Ask the question, "am I ready to let go and let God?"

- Understand (often for the first time) that we don't have, nor do we need to have, all the answers.

- Acknowledge that we can turn things over to the care of our Higher Power, again and again.

- Watch others in recovery, acknowledge the changes in them as a result of Step Three, and become willing.

- Recognize that old feelings may be triggered by events happening today and ask for God's guidance.

- Remind ourselves that "things don't usually happen the way we plan them; they usually work out better!"

What Tools Work For Me?

Made a decision to turn our will and our lives
over to the care of God as we understood God.
—Step Three

These questions are intended to help you work Step Three:

- What does "made a decision" mean to me?

- How do I know when I need to let go? How do I let go?

- What does "as we understood God" mean to me?

- Am I ready to let go and let God have a hand in managing my life?

- What does "to the care of God" mean to me?

- What does "turning it over" mean to me?

- Is this where I let go of results? How does letting go of results help us to work this Step better?

- How can I be in touch with my Higher Power's will for me? In what ways does my Higher Power speak to me?

- What does "my will and my life" mean to me?

- If I cannot trust myself, how can I trust my Higher Power? How do I practice trusting?

NOTES

NOTES

NOTES

*The only requirement for membership in CoDA
is a desire for healthy and loving relationships.*
—Tradition Three

The program of Co-Dependents Anonymous is open to anyone with a desire for healthy and loving relationships. Because it is so broad in definition, Tradition Three allows each of us to belong. It helps us to stay out of our judgments about who should and should not attend meetings. We cannot touch, see, or prove whether anyone else has the desire referred to in this Tradition. It does not matter how we look or what we believe, whether we are young or old, what color we are, our religion, or socioeconomic class. Many of us have looked for reasons not to belong. Focusing on our differences has often covered up our fear of not belonging. This Tradition can help us acknowledge that each of us is deserving of recovery.

Many of us found this Tradition comforting when we heard these words at our first meeting. We are given the freedom to attend meetings even if we minimized our experience. We did not have to justify our membership in CoDA. Tradition Three frees us from having to work through our issues, or determine if we are codependent, before beginning our program of recovery. Even if we believe our codependency is our fault, even if we are in complete denial, we can still come to meetings.

We can become increasingly mindful of this Tradition as we work our program with other members. We can embrace this Tradition as it applies to our daily life and relationships with others and ourselves. "I have a desire for healthy and loving relationships" is a positive affirmation which can assist us in our application of this Tradition. Step Three and Tradition Three are direct, yet the directives can be difficult for us to take. We tend to put many things in front of this Tradition. We may battle with the desire to protect ourselves and to control others. As codependents, we may find having healthy relationships is new behavior. As we begin our recovery, we often struggle with our ideas of what "healthy" means.

Codependency can be a subtle disease. To have healthy and loving relationships, we must decide that this is truly what we want. Keeping this desire in our hearts and minds helps us to replace our desire to protect ourselves at all times and at all costs. Promise Three of our program states "I know a new freedom." We begin to feel this freedom when we make this decision to have healthy, loving relationships.

Before recovery, we lived life according to what others wanted in a relationship. By placing our desire for a healthy relationship with ourselves first, we are learning a new way of life. When we love and honor ourselves, we have healthier relationships with others. A loving relationship includes honesty, openness, willingness, acceptance, and taking care of ourselves so that we can go freely to others. We learn to release the need to be filled from the outside, learning instead to be filled from within, before coming into relationship with another. Loyalty to ourselves needs always to come first.

As we do our service work, we can remember to set healthy, functional boundaries. Again, we can keep Tradition Three, and our new ideas about healthy relationships, in our hearts and minds. If we are struggling with someone or something, we remember that we are working on being healthy. Although we may not always like what is happening, we can let go and love others. We can come to our service work with no expectations. We can release our desire to manipulate others. We learn to speak our truth appropriately, and to respect and listen to others.

The only requirement for membership in CoDA
is a desire for healthy and loving relationships.

—Tradition Three

These questions are intended to help you work Tradition Three:

- What is a healthy and loving relationship?

- What will it take for me to have healthy and loving relationships?

- Where do I learn what a healthy relationship is? Where might I find some examples?

- Which tools can help me to remember this Tradition?

- How do I incorporate this Tradition into my daily life?

- How does Tradition Three help me in doing my service work?

- What might this Tradition allow me to do that I don't currently do?

- What does "desire" mean to me?

- Do I desire healthy and loving relationships?

- Which needs of mine may be stronger than my desire for healthy and loving relationships? (i.e. controlling, people-pleasing, caretaking, etc.)

- What may prevent me from letting go of the needs I described in the question above?

NOTES

NOTES

NOTES

NOTES

Made a searching and fearless moral inventory of ourselves.
—Step Four

The first three Steps provide the foundation for our Fourth Step work. In Step One, we admitted that we are powerless over others. In Step Two, we came to believe in a power greater than ourselves. Then, in Step Three, we made a decision to turn our will and our lives over to the care of God, as we understood God. With this spiritual foundation, we now focus on Step Four. We get ready by talking with our sponsor, meditating, and praying.

As we start this process, we may want to consider the following questions:

• How can I use Steps One, Two, and Three to do Step Four?

• What does "fearless" mean to me?

• What does "moral inventory" mean to me?

• What tools might I use to help me take this inventory?

• Which of the formats listed on page 49 will I use to do my Fourth Step?

Step Four requires us to do "a searching and fearless moral inventory." This is the Step where we begin to see our part in our own lives and relationships. In our inventory, we include our behaviors and character defects that have been harmful. This Step is not an invitation to be overly critical or hurt ourselves, but rather an invitation to speak our truth. The inventory process is one of the most loving things we can do for ourselves. Although it may be painful to acknowledge and to put into writing the harm we have caused, it can be more painful to keep it festering inside.

As we prepare to do a Fourth Step, we put aside worrying about Step Five—we only do one Step at a time, in the order they are written. We let go of what others may think; this is about being honest with ourselves. For some of us, shame—about our lives, the way we were treated, or that which comes from believing the lies we were told as children—may have trapped us in a vicious cycle. But, if we never change our beliefs about ourselves, we never change our behaviors. It is the act of taking Step Four that offers us the possibility of understanding, and then releasing, our shame. We begin to see that we are not mistakes, but have only made mistakes.

In working Step Four, many codependents find that we share certain character defects. One of our most common controlling behaviors is our need to be right. We were taught that being right meant we were safe, powerful, and in control. It may feel frightening to imagine letting go of the need to be right, but this is an old behavior based on our childhood survival skills, and it no longer serves us well.

Obsession (or worry) is another characteristic we may have used to survive life. As a member shared, "If I can figure out everything that could possibly go wrong, then I can be prepared for anything. But the reality is, no matter how much obsessing I do, it is still not my plan."

Another common behavior codependents often share is incessantly judging and comparing ourselves as less than or more than. By judging, criticizing, and comparing, many of us believed we could protect ourselves and avoid feeling vulnerable.

As we list our codependent behaviors, we acknowledge and accept the feelings that come with them. We find that we can sit still with all our feelings, including the pain. This is a powerful Step, and we find touching base with our Higher Power, our sponsors, and others in recovery reassuring. Many of us experience our faith in a Higher Power growing stronger. We begin to trust ourselves and have faith in our recovery.

A personal inventory helps us examine how our codependency has kept us from ourselves. This Step is about faith in ourselves to be honest, as well as faith in our Higher Power. We acknowledge the loss and pain we have experienced. We recognize those behaviors which get in the way. We begin to have relationships with ourselves and others that are based on integrity. Understanding that recovery doesn't have a timetable, we accept that we heal in God's time.

Believing in a power greater than ourselves helps us to let go and turn our will and our lives over to the care of God, as we understand God. In our searching and fearless moral inventory, it is important that we also list our positive character traits: our strengths, values, assets, and talents. Many of us find it difficult to include our good qualities. In the past, it may have been implied that by focusing on our good qualities we were being conceited, boastful, or self-involved. In recovery, in order to bring balance to our Fourth Step work, we acknowledge the need to embrace our strengths and our positive character traits.

We may find ourselves returning to Step Four to clear up issues we were originally unaware of or to look at a specific behavior and uncover the truth behind it. This is not a one-time Step—this is a real part of our recovery. We work the Steps, over and over again, as often as needed.

We want recovery from our codependency. We want the freedom we've heard comes with a written inventory. So, we begin. Somewhere. Anywhere. We write.

Step Four is an action Step. The following are a variety of formats we can use to complete a written Fourth Step:

- Take the list of codependent patterns and precede each pattern with "how did I harm myself or others by..." (Example—How did I harm myself and/or others by putting others' wants and needs before my own?)

- Break down your history into age groups (infant to 5; 5 to 12; 12 to 18; and so on). What patterns of codependency do you see developing in each age group? What patterns of healthy behavior do you see in each age group?

- Fill out the Patterns and Characteristics Chart on page 52 & 53.

- Fill out the Fourth Step Chart on pages 54 & 55.

In addition to the above Fourth Step formats, we also need to explore our strengths, assets, and positive behaviors. As suggested in our text, *Co-Dependents Anonymous,* page 46, we can make a list to identify our positive, healthy, appropriate, and loving behaviors. Our list may include people who have experienced our strengths, assets, and positive behaviors; our feelings about our strengths, assets, and positive behaviors in these relationships; and when we behaved in healthier ways. Then we can see the progress we have made in our recovery.

- Fill out the Positive Attributes Chart on page 56.

Note: The 22 questions contained in the original Step Four section are now located at the back of the workbook, as they are not specific to Step Four. See pages 170 and 171.

PATTERNS AND CHARACTERISTICS OF CODEPENDENCE

The following checklist is offered as a tool to aid in self-evaluation. It may be particularly helpful to newcomers as they begin to understand codependency. It may aid those who have been in recovery a while to determine what traits still need attention and transformation.

Denial Patterns:
Codependents often. . .
- have difficulty identifying what they are feeling.
- minimize, alter, or deny how they truly feel.
- perceive themselves as completely unselfish and dedicated to the well-being of others.
- lack empathy for the feelings and needs of others.
- label others with their negative traits.
- think they can take care of themselves without any help from others.
- mask pain in various ways such as anger, humor, or isolation.
- express negativity or aggression in indirect and passive ways.
- do not recognize the unavailability of those people to whom they are attracted.

Low Self-esteem Patterns:
Codependents often. . .
- have difficulty making decisions.
- judge what they think, say, or do harshly, as never good enough.
- are embarrassed to receive recognition, praise, or gifts.
- value others' approval of their thinking, feelings, and behavior over their own.
- do not perceive themselves as lovable or worthwhile persons.
- seek recognition and praise to overcome feeling less than.
- have difficulty admitting a mistake.
- need to appear to be right in the eyes of others and may even lie to look good.
- are unable to identify or ask for what they need and want.
- perceive themselves as superior to others.
- look to others to provide their sense of safety.
- have difficulty getting started, meeting deadlines, and completing projects.
- have trouble setting healthy priorities and boundaries.

Compliance Patterns:
Codependents often. . .
- are extremely loyal, remaining in harmful situations too long.
- compromise their own values and integrity to avoid rejection or anger.
- put aside their own interests in order to do what others want.
- are hypervigilant regarding the feelings of others and take on those feelings.
- are afraid to express their beliefs, opinions, and feelings when they differ from those of others.
- accept sexual attention when they want love.
- make decisions without regard to the consequences.
- give up their truth to gain the approval of others or to avoid change.

Control Patterns:

Codependents often. . .

- believe people are incapable of taking care of themselves.
- attempt to convince others what to think, do, or feel.
- freely offer advice and direction without being asked.
- become resentful when others decline their help or reject their advice.
- lavish gifts and favors on those they want to influence.
- use sexual attention to gain approval and acceptance.
- have to feel needed in order to have a relationship with others.
- demand that their needs be met by others.
- use charm and charisma to convince others of their capacity to be caring and compassionate.
- use blame and shame to exploit others emotionally.
- refuse to cooperate, compromise, or negotiate.
- adopt an attitude of indifference, helplessness, authority, or rage to manipulate outcomes.
- use recovery jargon in an attempt to control the behavior of others.
- pretend to agree with others to get what they want.

Avoidance Patterns:

Codependents often. . .

- act in ways that invite others to reject, shame, or express anger toward them.
- judge harshly what others think, say, or do.
- avoid emotional, physical, or sexual intimacy as a way to maintain distance.
- allow addictions to people, places, and things to distract them from achieving intimacy in relationships.
- use indirect or evasive communication to avoid conflict or confrontation.
- diminish their capacity to have healthy relationships by declining to use the tools of recovery.
- suppress their feelings or needs to avoid feeling vulnerable.
- pull people toward them, but when others get close, push them away.
- refuse to give up their self-will to avoid surrendering to a power greater than themselves.
- believe displays of emotion are a sign of weakness.
- withhold expressions of appreciation.

Patterns and Characteristics Chart

	PATTERN	HOW I HURT MYSELF	HOW I HURT OTHERS
SAMPLE	*Deny feelings*	*Deny my pain, sadness, joy. Others never see me as I really am. Isolated from others, lack of intimacy.*	*Deny their feelings, project my anger on others, being dishonest, attempt to control others' feelings.*

Patterns and Characteristics Chart

	PATTERN	HOW I HURT MYSELF	HOW I HURT OTHERS

Fourth Step Chart (from the CoDA Book)

Person	My codependent behaviors & reactions	My feelings that drove those behaviors	Consequences to the person, myself, & the relationship	My feelings about my behaviors & consequences
Mother	I made up lies to get her to give me money when I was broke 3 different times.	Shame about being irresponsible for my own finances. Fear of her judgment of me. Fear and anger about having to be financially responsible and having to get help.	Abandonment and neglect of my own financial responsibilities kept me financially and emotionally dependent on her. Manipulated her to be financially responsible for me. Kept me in the child role in our relationship and not equal.	Sad, ashamed, guilty.
Father	Stayed resentful, angry, and bitter about his sexual, verbal, and physical abuses of me without seeking help or resolving these. (He would pretend everything was fine when I was with him.) Etc.	Fear, anger, and shame about facing these issues. Fear of being abused or abandoned by him if I told him I was in CoDA or therapy. Fear of being labeled crazy and of being the "bad guy" in the family.	Continued loss of love and intimacy with him. Risk of my kids acting out my emotional secrets about him. Abandoned and neglected my own feelings about this. Needed to use anger, resentment, and bitterness to cover my hurt, fear and shame about being abused. Didn't learn to stand up for myself either with him directly or in some healthy way to gain a sense of empowerment with abusive men.	Lonely, sad, ashamed, scared and angry.
Joan (wife)	She raged at me at the park and I stayed silent for a couple days.	Fear and terror of her raging or abandoning me if I stood up to her. Fear she might look for someone else. Fear and anger that she would make me out to be the wrong one.	Abandoned and neglected my own feelings about this. Neglected myself and the relationship by not standing up for myself. Enabled her to continue raging. Controlled her through silence. Maintained lack of intimacy by punishing her with silence.	Lonely, sad, scared, ashamed, guilty.
Bonnie (daughter)	A couple days after Joan raged at me in the park, I raged and dumped all over Bonnie for not emptying the trash. Everything was fine between Joan and me after that.	Months of anger, resentment, pain, and shame about Joan's raging that I never shared with Joan or addressed at all.	I abandoned and neglected my feelings about Joan's behavior and raging. I reinforced the role for Bonnie as my emotional scapegoat. I drove Bonnie and I further apart. I reinforced fear and lack of trust in Bonnie toward me. I reinforced the message to Bonnie that raging is part of a relationship and it is OK.	Sad, ashamed, guilty, scared.
Allen (Boss, friend)	He told my co-workers about something confidential that I shared with him, and I became angry and called in sick the next day, so I wouldn't have to face them.	Fear that I might be fired if I told him how angry I was. Fear of losing the friendship if I told him how angry I was. Fear of him reacting to me in front of my co-workers. Fear of being judged by him and any co-workers as being too sensitive. Pain that my friend broke my confidence.	I abandoned and neglected my own feelings. Loss of trust and integrity in myself to stand up for myself and in him. Loss of intimacy with my friend. Loss of integrity within my friendship by not being honest. I reinforced the value that it's OK for people to violate my confidences.	Sad, lonely, angry, guilty, ashamed, scared.

Fourth Step Chart (from the CoDA Book)

Person	My codependent behaviors & reactions	My feelings that drove those behaviors	Consequences to the person, myself, & the relationship	My feelings about my behaviors & consequences

Positive Attributes Chart

Attribute	Action or Behavior	Feelings	Progress in Recovery

Step Four —

In this moment, I am willing to see myself as I truly am: a growing, unfolding, spiritual being. I separate who I am from what I've done, knowing that the real me is emerging—loving, joyful, and whole.

NOTES

_____

_____

_____

_____

_____

_____

_____

_____

_____

_____

_____

_____

_____

_____

_____

_____

_____

_____

_____

_____

NOTES

NOTES

NOTES

NOTES

NOTES

NOTES

NOTES

Each group should remain autonomous, except in matters affecting other groups or CoDA as a whole.

—Tradition Four

In Step Four, we take our own individual inventory. In Tradition Four, we can use the inventory process to evaluate our group's effect on other meetings or on CoDA as a whole. We can do this by considering how our group's behaviors and attitudes affect the Fellowship. We may also choose to take time at a meeting or group level to join together to assess whether we are supporting CoDA as a whole. We use the Steps and Traditions as guides to search our hearts in this process.

The creativity of our meetings can flourish because of our commitment to autonomy in this Tradition. As a result, various meeting formats exist to support us in recovery: On-line, phone, Step and Tradition, CoDA Book study, speaker, writing, coed, women's, men's, gay and lesbian, and more. Codependents may hear the message of recovery better in one type of meeting than in another. We respect each meeting's right to autonomy and to carry the message according to its group conscience. This diversity, created by autonomy, helps meet our individual needs and those of the CoDA community.

As much as we value autonomy, we value unity more. In this Tradition, we acknowledge we are part of a greater whole—the Fellowship of Co-Dependents Anonymous. Any decision we make as a group should be centered in our common welfare. Because the Steps, Traditions, Preamble, and Welcome define the CoDA program and our message of recovery, they are read at every meeting as written. The structure and consistency of our Fellowship's message needs to be something on which we can depend. The knowledge that a meeting's basic structure is the same, no matter where we go, provides safety for us. This structure and its emphasis on the basic tools of recovery are essential to both the newcomer and those who have time in the program. Using literature in our meetings which is not CoDA Conference endorsed can detract from CoDA unity and prevent newcomers from hearing CoDA's basic message of recovery.

When reflecting on the Fourth Tradition and the autonomy of our groups, it is also important to ask ourselves whether our meetings are accessible to the newcomer. Structuring our meetings in ways that maximize the ability of the newcomers to grasp the basic tools of recovery, as well as providing a welcoming atmosphere, support the continued strength of our Fellowship. Sponsors, phone lists, CoDA Conference endorsed literature, and the willingness to take service commitments also support our primary purpose and CoDA as a whole.

It is not always easy to know what will affect other groups or CoDA as a whole. However, by applying the Steps and Traditions, we do our best to support both autonomy and unity. We look at issues that arise in our groups and ask ourselves to remember our responsibility to the program. For instance, how a meeting uses its Seventh Tradition funds is a matter of autonomy, but we gain clarity by reviewing all the Steps and Traditions and linking our decisions to CoDA as a whole. We realize our reliance on the service structure of the CoDA Fellowship. Our Seventh Tradition donations fund such basics as meeting lists, phone lines, literature production, and delegate service. Thus, we review our financial responsibilities, not only to our meeting, but also to the service structure of CoDA. In this way, we acknowledge that CoDA communities, local, regional, national, and international are all part of the definition of CoDA as a whole.

Sharing our experience, strength, and hope at the meeting level and in our service work is a positive example of how our autonomous actions contribute to the well-being of CoDA. When doing service, we speak and act on behalf of those we serve. In meetings, we do our best to remember the worldwide Fellowship of Co-Dependents Anonymous and hold in our hearts the reality that we are part of this greater whole.

Each group should remain autonomous, except in matters affecting
other groups or CoDA as a whole.

—Tradition Four

These questions are intended to help you work Tradition Four:

- What is "CoDA as a whole?" How is my group related to the CoDA Fellowship?

- What does group autonomy mean?

- How can I respect the autonomy of a CoDA group, even if it isn't what I like or want?

- Is it difficult for me or my group to embrace the concept of CoDA as a whole? If yes, why?

- How can using non-Conference endorsed literature at a meeting be harmful to CoDA as a whole?

- What role does Tradition Four play in service work? How can my actions in my sponsorship and my service work affect CoDA as a whole?

- How can I, or my group, help support other codependents and/or CoDA groups in their autonomy? How do I, or my group, contribute to the CoDA Fellowship?

- How does reading the Steps, Traditions, Preamble, and Welcome at every meeting support CoDA?

- What individual actions might I take if I believe that the Traditions are not being upheld?

- Are CoDA service boards autonomous groups?

- How do Step Four and Tradition Four relate to one another?

NOTES

NOTES

NOTES

*Admitted to God, to ourselves, and to another human being
the exact nature of our wrongs.*

—Step Five

Step Five directs us to take specific action and make three very important connections. The first of these connections is with our Higher Power. The order of the Fifth Step reinforces a basic truth of recovery: our relationship with God comes first. We can take time in prayer and meditation to open our hearts and communicate with the God of our understanding about the exact nature of our wrongs. Many of us choose to make a list of our codependent behaviors and beliefs from our Fourth Step before talking with our Higher Power. This level of honesty can be an intimate and powerful experience. We can be comforted that there are no secrets between ourselves and our Higher Power. We begin to be relieved of the burden of our secrets and learn to trust our Higher Power even more. This Step helps us understand that our Higher Power loves and cares for us just as we are.

Step Five instructs us to make our second connection with ourselves and admit the exact nature of our wrongs to ourselves. Though at first it may seem we have already accomplished this in the course of completing an inventory, the Fifth Step guides us to solidify the truths we have uncovered. We may choose to read our inventory out loud to ourselves to reflect upon the nature of what we have discovered. Admitting the exact nature of our wrongs is more than repeating to ourselves what we have written; instead, we take the truth of our history and our codependency into our hearts. Giving the Fifth Step to ourselves, and looking at our self-defeating behavior and the harm we have caused ourselves and others, may put us in touch with the exact nature of our wrongs as never before. As we do this, we can see the pain caused by our denial. An honest Fifth Step supports us in our recovery and helps us understand why our lives were unmanageable. Admitting our wrongs to ourselves helps break through to greater honesty, self-awareness, and acceptance.

The final instruction of Step Five requires us to connect with another human being and admit the exact nature of our wrongs. Most of us accomplish this task by reading our inventory to a person who feels safe to us. We seek out someone who will actively listen without shaming or judging, who will listen with compassion and caring. This person could be our sponsor or someone else whose recovery program we respect: a close friend, a spiritual advisor, a therapist, or a Step study group of recovering codependents. Trusting the Steps and acknowledging that this process has worked for others can help us push through our fear. As we do our Fifth Step work, we recognize our codependent behavior patterns, where they came from, and the harm they have caused. Doing the Fifth Step begins to open the door to truth, joy, and freedom.

Remembering we can take care of ourselves and ask for what we need supports us in working this Step. We can set boundaries with the person we have chosen to share with. For example, we may ask them to listen without comment or to provide feedback. We can establish the length of time the work will take as well as where we wish it to take place. Trusting that our Higher Power is with us allows us to feel safe as we share the exact nature of our wrongs with another human being.

Step Five opens the door to truth and freedom. Step Five teaches us to be vulnerable and to trust. Step Five is about letting go.

Following are some gifts of completing a Fifth Step:

- When we talk about our codependency, we gain clarity concerning our own behavior—for instance, our need to control, our moods, our need to be right, our need to defend.
- We can let go of old behaviors and learn to be accountable and responsible.
- Our spirits are lifted as we share our truth.
- We experience freedom as we let go of our secrets.
- We enjoy the freedom and comfort of knowing we are not alone.
- We let go of old belief systems. For example, we do not die if we tell the truth, we do not disintegrate if we admit we are wrong, and we finally talk about our family secrets with people whom we trust.
- We accept the past.
- We build trust.

Receiving a Fifth Step:

Receiving a Fifth Step is a simple process. We simply receive it. Before listening, however, we may need to set some boundaries. For example, we can:

- practice detachment.
- keep our focus on the personal inventory.
- respect how and where the other person chooses to present this Step.
- listen without arguing, judging, or assuming.
- accept where the other person is for today.
- set aside ample time, without interruption.

It can be helpful and comforting to share a prayer to add to the spiritual reality of this work both before and after a Fifth Step. We bring our own Higher Power in as we listen, and we know we will be provided with whatever we need.

*Admitted to God, to ourselves, and to another human being
the exact nature of our wrongs.*
—Step Five

These questions are intended to help you work Step Five:

- Is it hard for me to work Step Five? Why?

- How can I let go of my fears of being judged or shamed when sharing my Fifth Step?

- What does "admitted" mean to me?

- What does "exact nature of our wrongs" mean to me?

- What does it mean to me to give my Fifth Step to God, myself, and another human being?

- Why is it important to admit my faults privately in my meditation and prayers?

- How can I let go of the need to defend my actions so that I can admit the truth?

- How will I bring my Higher Power into my Fifth Step?

- How do I trust another person with the information contained in my Fifth Step?

- What are some boundaries I would set for working my Fifth Step? What are some boundaries I would set in receiving someone's Fifth Step?

- When receiving a Fifth Step, what do I do when the person begins to stray from his/her own inventory and begins to take someone else's inventory?

NOTES

NOTES

NOTES

Each group has but one primary purpose—to carry its
message to other codependents who still suffer.

—Tradition Five

Tradition Five sets a boundary by establishing that each CoDA group "has but one primary purpose—to carry its message to other codependents who still suffer." This very simple directive reminds us that CoDA is a simple program. We are here for one reason—to recover from codependency. We support each other in this simplicity by keeping our focus on CoDA's primary purpose. As we carry the message, our groups do not get into or manage any one person's individual recovery.

"Primary" refers to what we consider the most important principle—the one that comes before all others. The survival and growth of our program depends upon our willingness to carry the message of hope and recovery by using the Steps and following the Traditions. Codependents who still suffer include people who have never attended a meeting, CoDA newcomers, and old-timers alike. We all need to share the message of recovery to gain and maintain our recovery. Tradition Five creates a responsibility for each group to uphold our Fellowship's primary purpose. Although our methods of carrying the message may vary among meetings, the primary purpose of all our groups remains the same.

Our newest members are a very important part of Tradition Five. Newcomers are often searching for ways to understand and find relief from codependency issues. Having current members welcome and speak to newcomers provides a supportive atmosphere. So does having CoDA literature and phone lists available. All of these efforts are ways to carry the message of recovery. Cliques and popularity contests have no place in CoDA; they divert us from our primary purpose and are dangerous to all members of the group. Losing focus on our primary purpose deprives a still suffering codependent of the CoDA message. The Fifth Tradition serves as a spiritual reminder when we have strayed from our purpose. When we share our experience, strength, and hope with our newer members, our own recovery is enhanced.

Honestly sharing what life was like before recovery, the tools we have used in recovery, and what life is like for us now supports Tradition Five. We share our struggles and our triumphs. We wonder how long any of us would have stayed if we had not heard the hope and seen changes occur in those around us. We practice Tradition Five whenever we share in our meetings, with sponsees or sponsors, with friends and family members, or with members of the public.

Supporting each other in recovery is another way that we carry the message. We can make and receive outreach calls and talk with one another after our meetings. Tradition Five helps us understand that by being an example of recovery, we are carrying the message.

In addition to CoDA meetings, we form local, regional, national, and international service groups to carry the message of recovery. Service commitments to these groups include providing public service information about CoDA, providing outreach to hospitals and institutions, and distributing literature.

These are powerful ways to reach the codependent who still suffers, some of whom may not be able to get to a meeting or even know of CoDA. Making commitments within these groups also provides us with an opportunity to live Tradition Five. Our primary purpose is to carry the message; it is through sharing and hearing the message that we recover.

Each group has but one primary purpose—to carry its message to other codependents who still suffer.

—Tradition Five

These questions are intended to help you work Tradition Five:

- Why is there "but one primary purpose" for our group?

- How can I keep my focus on our primary purpose?

- What do I believe is the message?

- What does it mean to me to "carry the message?" How do I do it?

- How does my CoDA group carry the message?

- If our group has strayed from our primary purpose, how can we focus back on it?

- How does sharing my experience, strength, and hope carry the message to those who still suffer?

- How can I carry this message to people I don't know?

- How does the Fifth Step relate to the Fifth Tradition?

- How was the message carried to me?

NOTES

NOTES

NOTES

Were entirely ready to have God remove
all these defects of character.

—Step Six

Having identified our character defects in Step Four, and having shared them with God, ourselves, and another human being in Step Five, we become ready for God to remove them in Step Six.

Accepting our defects with humility allows our healing to begin, and honesty with our Higher Power and ourselves plays a major role in becoming entirely ready. "Entirely" means completeness, which means letting go of trying to control our defects. We are asked to be entirely ready as we work our program, writing, sharing, meditating, and asking for knowledge of our Higher Power's will in our lives. Continuing to be entirely ready becomes a way of life, not a one-time event.

Defects can be seen as behaviors and beliefs that stand in our way. Defects of character are not who we are spiritually; they are codependent behaviors that we have used to survive life. In becoming entirely ready, we learn to own our defects. When we ask our Higher Power to guide us and we trust in this process, we have a spiritual experience. The keys for Step Six are strong faith, trust, and a connection to our Higher Power.

This Step does not say how or when our defects will be removed. We can use Step Three to remember that it is not our plan. It is our Higher Power's plan for us that we accept, even when we do not understand. This is our Higher Power's will. Many times we realize a defect has been removed and we are not sure when it happened. Again, we are reminded that recovery is a journey, not a destination.

When we recognize a character defect with which we are struggling, there are tools to help us. We can speak to our sponsor, attend a meeting, write in our journal, and ask our Higher Power for guidance. We can use positive affirmations if we feel overwhelmed as we work this Step. We recognize that Step Six is clearly about progress, not perfection; it is not about how far we have come, nor how far we have to go, but about being on the path of recovery. We invite our Higher Power into our lives and we let go of the results. As we truly surrender to this plan, we may or may not see progress. Our job is to continue to work our program, one day at a time, to the best of our ability.

We relied upon these character defects for many years. Because of this, we struggle to let go and be entirely ready. Indeed, it takes effort and is not easy to let go of old "friends" such as obsessing, the need to be right, people-pleasing, judgment, fear, procrastination, and perfectionism. We become entirely ready, so that our Higher Power can remove our character defects. Step Six is another Step that reminds us how important it is to practice letting go.

Were entirely ready to have God remove
all these defects of character.

—Step Six

These questions are intended to help you work Step Six:

- How do I become "entirely ready?"

- How does my trust in my Higher Power help me become ready?

- When will the character defects be removed? How are these defects removed?

- What does a defect of character feel like?

- What are "defects of character?" What are my defects of character?

- Does the phrase "defects of character" make me feel defensive? Why?

- How can I overcome any resistance I feel to hearing I have defects of character?

- What does it feel like to be entirely ready?

- What prompts me to justify or minimize these defects of character?

- How do the Steps help me to accept my defects?

- What may I be gaining by holding on to a particular defect of character?

- Why is Step Six a crucial bridge between Steps Five and Seven?

NOTES

NOTES

NOTES

NOTES

A CoDA group ought never endorse, finance, or lend the CoDA
name to any related facility or outside enterprise,
lest problems of money, property, and prestige
divert us from our primary spiritual aim.

—Tradition Six

Tradition Five teaches us that we come together for no other reason but to recover from codependency. Tradition Six refers to our "primary spiritual aim" for the first time. The spiritual foundation of our program becomes clear as we continue to study our Traditions.

With that purpose in mind, we keep ourselves from engaging in outside obligations and responsibilities. If we lend our name to a building, recovery facility, church, or hospital, we create an obligation outside our program. Outside obligations divert us from our primary spiritual aim. Our focus is always on our spiritual aim, spreading the word to those who still suffer from codependency. If we lose that focus, our program's spiritual foundations will be lost.

Within the Fellowship, we recognize the need to separate material issues from our spiritual aim. We avert problems of money, property, and prestige by assigning legal and financial responsibilities to a Board of Trustees. In our history, we have experienced the distraction created when the wisdom of this Tradition was ignored and we mixed the spiritual and the material. We also respect the wisdom gained from the history of Alcoholics Anonymous, the program we were patterned after.

We are a Twelve Step Fellowship, and therefore we do not endorse books, programs, or individuals outside of the Fellowship. To work CoDA's program of recovery, we recommend using our Twelve Steps, Twelve Traditions, and CoDA Conference endorsed literature. Educational workshops within our program also honor and endorse the CoDA Steps, Traditions, and literature. This framework applies to all CoDA activities, such as business meetings, conferences, conventions, and regular CoDA meetings. As sponsors or other trusted servants, we are responsible for keeping our program within the Steps and Traditions. Out of respect for Tradition Six, we never endorse or lend the CoDA name to outside enterprises.

Another way we can be diverted from our primary spiritual aim is when professionals begin or join a CoDA meeting for their own personal gain, instead of coming to a meeting for their own recovery. The prestige of using last names of well-known people also diverts us. In our disease, we may believe someone with prestige would be better able to help us in our recovery. This is a humble program, and there is no place for prestige or personal gain. The power of our program is in the simplicity of one codependent sharing experience, strength, and hope with another.

*A CoDA group ought never endorse, finance, or lend the CoDA
name to any related facility or outside enterprise,
lest problems of money, property, and prestige
divert us from our primary spiritual aim.*

—Tradition Six

These questions are intended to help you work Tradition Six:

- What is our primary spiritual aim?

- How can issues of money, property, or prestige divert us from our primary spiritual aim? What other issues might divert us?

- Why is it important not to endorse non-CoDA literature, workshops, or people? As a sponsor? As a CoDA member? As a trusted servant?

- How can using non-CoDA Conference endorsed literature in a meeting or workshop divert us from our primary spiritual aim?

- How can we be creative in a workshop and stay within this Tradition?

- What harm is there in allowing a treatment facility to use our name?

- In what ways might people misuse a meeting for personal gain? How does this divert the meeting from our primary spiritual aim?

- What is my responsibility to the group when I believe we have lost focus on our primary spiritual aim?

- What is the specific purpose of Tradition Six within the framework of the Twelve Traditions?

NOTES

NOTES

NOTES

NOTES

Humbly asked God to remove our shortcomings.

—Step Seven

The direction in this Step is simple. It is not results oriented; we ask and then let go. With the acceptance of a loving Higher Power in our lives, we become willing to believe our shortcomings will be removed.

By the time we get to Step Seven, we may have strong feelings about our shortcomings and our past behaviors. We recognize the harm we have caused ourselves and see our inability to change our behavior through self-will. We realize that our shortcomings are harmful; therefore, we humbly ask our Higher Power to remove them.

Asking that our shortcomings be removed may be scary. In our childhoods, when we were vulnerable and admitted our imperfections, terrible things happened. Because of this history, it may never occur to us to be vulnerable and ask something of our Higher Power. We may still be making choices today based on our old survival behavior. In the past, we may have been taught, "If it is to be, it is up to me," and/or "Never let anyone see you are struggling." We may have been taught we couldn't rely on anyone or anything, except our own abilities and ourselves. As recovering codependent adults, we ask God to remove our shortcomings, including our fears, self-criticism, and perfectionism—then we let go. In working Step Seven, we choose living, loving ourselves, and working our recovery program.

We trust our Higher Power. We accept that we have shortcomings. We ask that our shortcomings be removed.

The following are some examples of shortcomings we may ask God to remove:

- procrastination
- needing to do something about what we are feeling
- belief that we are in control
- fear of letting go and trusting
- fear of what others may think or feel about us
- fear of others' anger
- dishonesty
- manipulation (overt or covert)
- self-abuse
- reacting rather than acting
- our need to be right
- our need to do it ourselves, without any help
- our inability to ask for help
- our desire for others to do it our way
- perfectionism
- addictions
- guilt
- resentments

- self-righteousness
- isolation
- shame
- self-abandonment
- belief that we have to act on our feelings

When we share at meetings, we gain clarity about our self-defeating behaviors. When others share, we find similarities in our patterns of codependency. Speaking the truth and asking that our shortcomings be removed increases our awareness that a Higher Power is present in our lives. We accept that we are not perfect, realizing the truth that our Higher Power can remove our shortcomings and, by ourselves, we can't. We learn to focus on what our Higher Power wants for us on a daily basis.

Humbly asking God to remove our shortcomings does not necessarily mean being on our knees, although some of us seek out a church, temple, or other peaceful or sacred place. Being humble, we accept our Higher Power's plan for us. Being humble, we also accept our place in the universe—not better, not worse, not bigger, not smaller. We may have learned in childhood that humility meant humiliation; today we believe differently. We may not have known then that we had a right to ask our Higher Power for help. Now we learn to be willing to let go and let God. We learn to accept ourselves, without being controlled by what others think of us. We accept the past and the messes we created by trying to do it all ourselves. We learn humility can be a good thing, bringing good feelings. God will do for us what we cannot do for ourselves.

With humility, we can ask our Higher Power for help with all things. Our Higher Power has seen all we have done in our lives and loves us just as we are today. We accept that.

Humbly asked God to remove our shortcomings.
—Step Seven

These questions are intended to help you work Step Seven:

- What does "Humbly asked God" mean to me?

- What fears do I have about my shortcomings being removed? List your fears.

- What are my shortcomings?

- How is "humbly asking" different from being "entirely ready?"

- How does the belief that I am a shameful person keep me in my codependency?

- What does humility mean to me?

- How does one humbly ask?

- How can I be more accepting as I work Step Seven?

- In what ways might Step Seven assist me in my recovery?

- How can I let go of my self-will as I work Step Seven?

- Does the affirmation, "God knows everything about me and loves me as I am," help me in this Step?

NOTES

NOTES

NOTES

Every CoDA group ought to be fully self-supporting,
declining outside contributions.

—Tradition Seven

Our Seventh Tradition is about CoDA meetings and CoDA service groups being fully self-supporting. One way a meeting or group supports itself is financially, which is crucial to the survival and growth of CoDA. Another, and equally crucial way of being self-supporting, is through our service work.

Each of us depends on meetings to be there when we need one. The CoDA Fellowship relies on a continuously changing array of volunteers to do service work. What would happen to CoDA if no one did any service? CoDA would cease to exist. When CoDA members join together to create a meeting or group, it is important that everyone is an equal participant with equal say, and that the responsibility for that group is shared by all. If one individual is doing too much, it takes away from the equal participation of others. Conversely, if an individual does too little, this burdens the rest of the group. Doing our individual part in service, as guided by our Higher Power, supports Tradition Seven.

Being of service is important to CoDA and to our individual recovery, not what we are doing in service. All service positions at all levels are equal. For example, serving as the literature person at your home meeting is just as important as being a CoDA committee chair. As we acknowledge our individual responsibility to the CoDA meeting or group, we also acknowledge that we are a group, with responsibilities of being self-supporting. For instance, if there are not enough volunteers to produce a CoDA community newsletter, we stop publishing it. If no one volunteers to make coffee, there is no coffee.

Groups are self-supporting, in part, when:

- meetings/groups pay for their meeting space
- meetings/groups make donations to CoDA's service structure (local, regional, national, and international)
- members share experience, strength, and hope on a regular basis
- service positions are filled
- service positions are rotated

Self-supporting means that groups look within themselves for funding. Accepting outside contributions creates outside affiliation as discussed in Tradition Six. *(A CoDA group ought never endorse, finance, or lend the CoDA name to any related facility or outside enterprise, lest problems of money, property, and prestige divert us from our primary spiritual aim.)* Adherence to Tradition Seven protects CoDA groups from outside influence or obligations. To illustrate the problem of a meeting not being fully self-supporting, consider the following:

In a member's will, it was asked that money be given each year to a CoDA community group to help spread the word to the Fellowship. As there are no guidelines for CoDA on this kind of matter, the initial group conscience of the CoDA community group decided that if it was in his will, it would be done. Questions of what to do with this money (spend it, save it, how much to spend, pass it on) diverted the group from being fully self-supporting, as it had been before the bequest. In this example, we came to believe that the bequest had affected the responsibility of the group to be self-supporting.

If we find ourselves attending a CoDA group that is struggling because of non-support, we may choose to do a group inventory as a tool to determine what solutions may be available. As part of that inventory process, we may ask ourselves in what ways we contribute to CoDA in terms of money; time; attention; enthusiasm; energy; trust; respect; compassion; support; and sharing our experience, strength, and hope. Service can be the beginning of a journey out of isolation and an opportunity to practice healthy relationships as a member of the group.

Every CoDA group ought to be fully self-supporting,
declining outside contributions.

—Tradition Seven

These questions are intended to help you work Tradition Seven:

- How can meetings/service groups be "self-supporting?"

- What does self-supporting mean to me? In my meeting? In my home? Give examples of each.

- In my personal life, am I self-supporting? If not, what can I do to become more self-supporting?

- In what ways can this Tradition apply to our service structure? (local, regional, national, or international)

- What is too much service for me? In what ways may this be harmful?

- In what ways may it be harmful to the meeting if I take on too many service commitments?

- What am I looking to gain by doing more than my fair share? What am I protecting myself from by not doing my fair share?

- What constitutes an *outside contribution* in my meeting?

- What do I believe the limit should be on a financial donation from a member? Why?

- Do I allow my family and friends the freedom of being self-supporting? Do I believe I deserve this same freedom?

- How does Step Seven relate to Tradition Seven?

NOTES

NOTES

NOTES

*Made a list of all persons we had harmed and became willing
to make amends to them all.*

—Step Eight

The first part of Step Eight asks us to list all the people we have harmed, regardless of the circumstances. The Step work we have done to this point can be helpful and supportive as we identify those we have harmed and realize how our behaviors have hurt others and ourselves. Often, it is easier to see how we have harmed others. Sometimes it takes a spiritual two-by-four in order for us to admit just how harmful we have been to ourselves. If shame or guilt overwhelms us, we can rely on our Higher Power and remember our decision to live God's will. We find peace when we let go and trust our Higher Power. We no longer waste energy pushing down the memories or the feelings.

In the second part of Step Eight, we are asked only to become willing to make amends. We are not asked to make amends. In this Step, we do not need to decide how or when the amends will be made. Keeping this in mind, we can work with our Higher Power on becoming willing.

If we feel frightened by being honest and feeling vulnerable, we can rely on Steps One, Two, and Three to support us as we become willing. We can ask our Higher Power to help us let go of obsessing over making our amends, and with the support of our Higher Power, we can let go of the belief that harm will come if we tell the truth. The fear of being wrong or of being judged can be offset with a positive affirmation such as, "I admit my mistakes and learn from them." If resentment, anger, and feelings about others seem to be holding us back from working this Step, we remember that we are powerless over others. Believing in a power greater than ourselves will restore us to sanity.

As we write our list of those we have harmed, we remember our Higher Power and acknowledge our Higher Power already knows everything we have done. We may want to make lists from different perspectives, like the harm that we have caused ourselves, the harm that we have caused others, or the resentments that we hold.

The following may be ways we have harmed others or ourselves:

- holding resentments
- acting out
- fearing intimacy
- manipulating others
- needing to be right
- cheating, lying, and stealing
- obsessing or worrying
- blaming and judging others
- emotionally abusing ourselves or others
- physically abusing ourselves or others
- neglecting our responsibilities

- creating financial stress
- abandoning ourselves
- separating from our spiritual selves

The list we make in Step Eight acknowledges our harmful behavior in a new way, and we become accountable to ourselves and our Higher Power for what we have done. We begin to understand how important it is to see our harmful behavior. We no longer have to hold on to the secrets of our past or live in denial of our past. We understand we have harmed because we were harmed. With this kind of honesty, change can begin; we can start to restore our relationships with others and ourselves in a healthy and loving way.

The list may grow as more is revealed and awareness is gained. When we acknowledge we no longer wish to ignore our feelings, we work this Step and find the possibility of relief encourages us to continue. Our recovery continues to bring awareness of old behaviors and ways we have harmed ourselves and others. We also become aware of how we continue old behaviors in our lives today. We stay open to what is revealed and we acknowledge we do not know everything about ourselves. We recognize our behaviors have an effect. This is why we work the Steps, over and over, to remain in the truth as it is revealed.

Made a list of all persons we had harmed and became willing to make amends to them all.

—Step Eight

These questions are intended to help you work Step Eight:

- What does become "willing to make amends" mean to me?

- How do I handle fear as I work this Step?

- Which Steps do I use as tools as I work Step Eight?

- How do I become willing?

- How can I forgive myself?

- What harm have I caused by believing I was better than, or less than, others?

- How do I get from feeling I am insignificant to recognizing I have harmed others?

- About whom do I feel hard-hearted, fearful, or defensive?

- In what ways have I harmed others?

- In what ways have I harmed myself?

- How did my dishonesty harm others or myself?

- Whom have I harmed because of my resentments?

- Whom have I harmed because of my need to control?

NOTES

NOTES

NOTES

Co-Dependents Anonymous should remain forever
nonprofessional, but our service centers
may employ special workers.

—Tradition Eight

This Tradition gives us an important guideline: CoDA should remain forever nonprofessional. This means CoDA meetings and service groups have no professional aspect. Thus, CoDA members with professional credentials participate in meetings only as recovering members of our Fellowship. We gather together as codependents for one purpose, to carry the message of recovery by sharing our experience, strength, and hope. This Tradition also helps us to maintain our equality and humility, valuing each other as fellow members in spiritual recovery.

As we do our service work for CoDA, we may find it necessary to employ special workers for some of the Fellowship's needs. These special workers fill positions that CoDA volunteers may not be able to fill because of time constraints, feasibility, or special skills. Special workers may include administrative help, accountants, and lawyers. As members of the Fellowship, we keep a personal recovery attitude rather than creating airs of superiority.

The members of our Fellowship who come forward to be of service do so in a nonprofessional way. Trusted servants are responsible to those they serve (an individual or community meeting or other CoDA group), doing only those jobs asked of them by that group. Trusted servants do not create their responsibilities. We remember that trusted servants are codependents in recovery and we do not look on them as professionals or as leaders. We also remember that for CoDA's purpose there is but one authority as defined in our Second Tradition, *a loving Higher Power as expressed to our group conscience.*

If some of our trusted servants lead professional lives, they have an obligation to establish a boundary, keeping their service in the program separate from their profession. In Tradition Six, we learned the importance of not being diverted by money, property, and prestige. Remaining nonprofessional helps all of us with this Tradition. It is often easy for codependents to be enamored of the prestige of a person's professional status. Being mindful of the servant position helps us remember our aim is a spiritual one, not a professional one. All of this protects our program so that members of our Fellowship experience their own spiritual recovery.

In our CoDA workshops, conferences, and conventions, we must remember that what members have to offer is their experience, strength, and hope. In CoDA, no one is paid to share, whether at meetings, as sponsors, or in any other Twelve Step activity. We do not offer advice or answers to other members. This nonprofessional approach creates safety for members. We take what we want and leave the rest. In our recovery from codependency, using the Twelve Steps and Twelve Traditions, we learn that we have our own answers within ourselves. Within this environment, each of us can experience the safety to work our own program at our own pace.

Using CoDA Conference endorsed literature supports our nonprofessional environment. Our program is based on CoDA's Twelve Steps, Twelve Traditions, and other CoDA literature written by members of our Fellowship sharing their experience, strength, and hope about recovery from codependency. Tradition Eight is an example of how our Traditions protect us from ourselves.

CoDA is a program based on the Twelve Steps and Twelve Traditions. We let go of dependence on others and receive guidance from our Higher Power. This guidance supports the spiritual nature of our program and is how we remain forever nonprofessional.

Co-Dependents Anonymous should remain forever
nonprofessional, but our service centers
may employ special workers.

—Tradition Eight

These questions are intended to help you work Tradition Eight:

- How does Tradition Eight support the spirituality of our program?

- Why is it important for CoDA to remain nonprofessional? What does this mean to me?

- How can I support my meeting in maintaining a nonprofessional environment?

- Why don't we employ professional speakers or workshop leaders?

- How does this Tradition apply to a meeting using literature that is not CoDA Conference endorsed?

- How does the second part of this Tradition relate to the first part?

- What are special workers? Under what circumstances would CoDA employ a special worker?

- Can special workers be someone who is not in CoDA?

- What might a service center do?

- Why is this Tradition important to the well-being of our program?

NOTES

NOTES

NOTES

Made direct amends to such people wherever possible,
except when to do so would injure them or others.

—Step Nine

The Step work we have done prepares us to take the action of Step Nine. We have written our moral inventory, acknowledged our defects of character, and have become aware of our codependent behavior. Continuing our recovery, we experience being entirely ready to have God work in our lives. We learn to humbly ask God to remove from us what no longer serves us. This brings us to a place of honesty as we work on our amends.

In the past, we may have minimized our effect on others. It is difficult to take responsibility for our actions if we believe our actions have no impact. In changing our attitudes and actions, we no longer believe that what we do is insignificant. In Step Eight, we were truthful with ourselves about our past behavior and made our list. Having done this honestly, we found that we were released from some of our shame. This work prepares us to be more honest as we begin to make our amends. Amends are our pure truth without blame, distraction, justification, or manipulation; we are taking responsibility for our experience. We understand that making amends also means we are truly committed to changing with the help of our Higher Power.

We support our commitment to recovery by making "parallel" amends to ourselves each time we make amends to someone else. For example, has our gossip about someone else harmed their reputation? Along with making an amends to them, we need to change our behavior by avoiding gossip. When we make an honest effort to change our own behavior, we become accountable and avoid engaging in harmful behaviors to ourselves and others. Then, we let go of the shame and forgive ourselves for our imperfections.

If we are thorough about this stage of our recovery, we consider ourselves important enough to include in our amends. For many of us, this is contrary to our disease which has often had us believing we mattered less than others. How do we make amends to ourselves? The answers to this can be as varied and creative as our members. When we truly contemplate the idea of making amends to ourselves, we understand that making these amends has the power to bring us healing and joy. We treat ourselves differently, and we do our best not to abandon ourselves. We value our own needs, and we consider what we want and how we feel to be equally important to the needs of others. However, in some situations, our needs are even more important to ourselves than what others may want.

Working on forgiveness before making amends is very important. As we let go of the past, accept the truth about it, and learn about our freedom of choice in recovery today, we begin to feel a new inner peace. Sometimes, this is our first experience of forgiveness. This opens the door to restoring relationships with ourselves and others. Without forgiveness, we harbor resentments and our amends may not be genuine. This is not a time to "act as if." Allowing our Higher Power to guide us supports us in being honest with ourselves and others. In times of confusion, it is helpful to talk to our sponsor or others in recovery to gain clarity and determine what is ours and what is not. We need to let go of the other person's part and be responsible for our part only. Making amends in this way gives us the experience of freedom from the burden of shame, guilt, and over-responsibility. Being free of resentment is an amends in and of itself.

As we prepare to make our amends, one way of caring for ourselves is to plan how we wish to deliver them. We can then share our plan and list with our sponsor or another trustworthy person. Listening to the experience, strength, and hope of others helps us think about how we are going to give our amends and to whom. In this Step, we are instructed to make direct amends wherever possible; sometimes, this may be to people with whom we do not necessarily feel safe. At these times, it may be inadvisable to make direct amends. We can work with our sponsor, for instance, to find a meaningful way to make direct amends that are safe and will not risk our well-being. In other cases, where we can make amends to the person directly, there are ways to care for ourselves. We can call a trusted person before and after, create a time boundary, ask for no feedback, and prepare ourselves beforehand to let go of results. Our Higher Power is with us, and we can remember that we are capable of taking care of ourselves.

Step Nine states that we make amends "wherever possible." However, we may owe amends to someone who has died, or whose whereabouts are not known, or where more harm may be caused than good. Sometimes, someone may refuse to hear an amends that we would like to make. As a substitute, we may write these amends in a journal and/or share them with a sponsor or someone unrelated to the circumstances. In other situations, we can bring good into today in ways we either could not or did not in the past. For example, if we owe an amends to a parent who is no longer with us, we can be kind to an older person who may need time and attention. If we are unable to make amends to our children, we might choose to volunteer at a local youth service or spend time with a young person who is in our lives. Often these types of amends are called "living amends," and practicing them can be a meaningful part of our recovery.

Some other ways we can make living amends to ourselves or others are:

- saying "no" in order to take care of ourselves

- expressing a differing opinion and letting go of our fears of what others may think

- listening to others and letting go of our belief that everyone needs to be the same and feel the same

- allowing others the dignity to live their lives in their own way

- living our lives differently because we are in recovery

Amends are not about getting things off our chest at the expense of others. They are not simply about clearing the air. Rather, they are spiritual exercises in humility whereby we are watchful of our attitudes and actions. Healthy behavior can be our most powerful amends; it is a testament to our recovery. This can be the greatest gift of Step Nine.

Made direct amends to such people wherever possible,
except when to do so would injure them or others.

—Step Nine

These questions are intended to help you work Step Nine:

- What are amends?

- How can I prepare for my amends work?

- What do I believe is the purpose of making amends?

- How do I decide whether my amends would injure others or myself?

- What is my motive for my amends?

- How can I forgive others prior to making amends? Is complete forgiveness necessary?

- How can I let go of expectations when making amends? Why is it important that I do so?

- How do I take care of myself when making amends? What tools or Steps do I use to keep it simple, safe, and clear?

- How might I make amends to myself?

- What alternative actions can I take if direct amends aren't possible?

- What does "living amends" mean to me?

NOTES

NOTES

NOTES

NOTES

NOTES

CoDA, as such, ought never be organized; but we may create service boards or committees directly responsible to those they serve.

—Tradition Nine

This Tradition protects the service structure of CoDA to serve the changing needs of the Fellowship by stating that CoDA, as such, ought never be organized. The Fellowship gives direction to the service boards made up of trusted servants, and the work is done accordingly. These trusted servants do not govern. There are no agendas, rules, or regulations that are enforced by them. Our guidance comes from the Steps, the Traditions, and our Higher Power as revealed to us through our group conscience process.

Each CoDA meeting is free to attend to the direct needs of its members within *The Twelve Traditions of Co-Dependents Anonymous.* Tradition Nine protects this freedom for each CoDA group. Each meeting or service group can support this Tradition by rotating service positions. By doing so, responsibilities are handed over and an active flow of service and energy exists. Rotating positions also prevents dominance from individuals that may lead to control and a more rigid, organized structure.

The Steps are our personal guides to spirituality while the Traditions guide our groups in the spiritual role of service work. Our Step work helps us with the application of this Tradition. One of the links between Step Nine and Tradition Nine is that both ask us to be responsible. In Step Nine, we become responsible to ourselves for our actions and acknowledge our right to be, think, and feel; we acknowledge others' right to do the same. In Tradition Nine, we accept our responsibility to trust the authority of the group conscience of those we are serving. We let go of our personal agendas and are reminded that the power in CoDA lies in our collective Higher Power and the group conscience of the Fellowship.

Sometimes, it is necessary to create boards or committees to fulfill the tasks of service. Some of these tasks include mailing out meeting lists, planning conferences and conventions, and maintaining phone service. CoDA's service structure is made up of volunteer service boards and committees serving the needs of the Fellowship at large. Some of the services provided internationally are creating literature, publishing and distributing literature, servicing CoDA's Web site, communication with the Fellowship, and handling finances. These boards or committees must be diligent in their direct responsibility to follow the group conscience of those they are serving.

Co-Dependents Anonymous, Incorporated (CoDA) and CoDA Resource Publishing, Incorporated (CoRe) are separate structures with certain legal duties to perform in being responsible for the matters of each respective corporation, but their common purpose is to serve the CoDA Fellowship. Some CoDA communities may incorporate to sign leases for rent requirements, to gain non-profit tax status, to handle insurance liability, and more. All these corporations must also be as free as possible of internal organization. Leaders hold positions of responsibility; the ultimate authority of all these groups is a group conscience. The Twelve Steps and Twelve Traditions of Co-Dependents Anonymous guide us all. In the interest of CoDA as a whole, Tradition Nine reminds us that CoDA is guided by the group conscience of the entire Fellowship, not the will of a few individuals.

CoDA, as such, ought never be organized; but we may create service boards or committees directly responsible to those they serve.

—Tradition Nine

These questions are intended to help you work Tradition Nine:

- What is the difference between an organization and a Fellowship?

- What does "organized" mean to me as used in this Tradition?

- What is the importance of letting go of my personal agenda when acting as a trusted servant?

- How can my Step work assist me in the application of Tradition Nine?

- Why does CoDA have committees and service boards?

- How does our informal structure help us in service work?

- How could my codependency keep me from being directly responsible to those I'm serving?

- How does CoDA's being a completely volunteer Fellowship affect my willingness to do service work?

- When doing service work, how can I remember I am directly responsible to those I'm serving? Why is this important?

- How does this Tradition support my recovery?

NOTES

NOTES

NOTES

Continued to take personal inventory and when we were wrong promptly admitted it.

—Step Ten

Step Ten asks that we continue taking personal inventories. This connects us to our program and helps us increase our awareness. This Step talks about a "personal" inventory and offers an additional tool for us. The moral inventory in Step Four helped us understand our history. A personal inventory helps us see the choices we are making now and the actions we are taking today. How are these choices and actions supporting us in our lives today? Are things going well, or poorly? When we have been wrong in our choices or actions, this Step tells us to admit it promptly. The wording of Step Ten offers a clear perspective on our being human. "When we were wrong" says that sometimes we are wrong. We are not—and cannot be—perfect. Thus, Step Ten supports our relationship to our Higher Power.

Developing a personal checklist is one way to work Step Ten. Although we may think of this Step as something we perform at the end of the day, many of us have found it useful to do a mid-day inventory. This can help us reconnect with ourselves and become centered as we move into our afternoon activities.

Some suggestions for a personal checklist might include:

- Am I living my Higher Power's will?
- Am I practicing gratitude?
- Did I do some form of prayer and/or meditation?
- Did I communicate in a healthy way today?
- If I let my codependent behavior take over today, what was that codependent behavior?
- Am I getting enough sleep and rest? Recreation?
- Did I exercise today—take a walk, swim, or do any other self-care activities?
- Am I eating a healthy diet?
- Did I honor my feelings today?
- Am I taking care of myself?

This Step supports us in staying current and present in our lives. By using the Tenth Step, we experience personal accountability on a daily basis. Have we completed what we said we would do today? Did we let go of codependent behaviors such as trying to change or trying to control others? Did we observe the positives and celebrate new behavior and recovery?

Having different feelings from another does not mean we are wrong. Using Step Ten helps us understand what is our part and what we are responsible for. This Step is not used to get approval, to be right, or solve our feeling of anxiety. In recovery, before we react, we slow down, look at a situation clearly, and then take action if needed.

We remind ourselves daily that it is human not to be perfect and that it is OK. Admitting that we are human, we are then free to focus on recovery. With our Higher Power, it is possible for us to change by being honest about our wrongs and admitting them. As we admit and let go, we are empowered to live God's will. We can forgive ourselves and develop a loving relationship with ourselves.

When we know that we have done wrong, it is good to act promptly before we talk ourselves out of it. When we are in doubt about our need to make amends, we can ask our Higher Power for clarity. When we admit our mistakes, we let go of the impossible goal of being perfect. When a person is not available to whom we can make amends directly, we can work with our sponsor or another CoDA member and our Higher Power. When we admit our wrongs, we experience a new freedom.

Step Ten teaches us to review our behavior regularly. The work we do in this Step helps us to increase our awareness and to understand where we need to practice new behavior. Being codependent is not something we can just stop doing, but through this Step we begin to live more honest and fulfilling lives. Step Ten is a daily anchor in our recovery process, which frees us from the bonds of codependency.

Continued to take personal inventory and when we were wrong promptly admitted it.

—Step Ten

These questions are intended to help you work Step Ten:

- What is the purpose of Step Ten?

- What does it mean to me to do a personal inventory? Is it different from a moral inventory? How?

- How does doing a Tenth Step enhance my recovery?

- Which codependent behaviors of mine would be good to include on a Tenth Step checklist?

- What is my list of positives for my Tenth Step today?

- Why is it important to list my positives and recovery experiences with my codependent behaviors?

- How do I know when I'm wrong? What behaviors do I exhibit?

- What prevents me from admitting my wrongs?

- Do I have a tendency to always think I'm wrong, or to always think I'm right? How does such behavior relate to this Step?

- How does this Step keep me humble?

- How does this Step assist me in letting go and living in the present?

- Am I willing to work this Step into my daily routine?

NOTES

NOTES

NOTES

CoDA has no opinion on outside issues; hence the CoDA name ought never be drawn into public controversy.

—Tradition Ten

Tradition Ten gives the CoDA Fellowship a direct guideline—CoDA has no opinion on outside issues. These words define a boundary for CoDA. By following this guideline, the Fellowship is able to avoid public controversy. As members of the Fellowship, we don't represent Co-Dependents Anonymous in public regarding any issue. CoDA has no opinions on anything outside of our Fellowship.

Just as we avoid controversy on a personal level by not giving advice to others, we avoid controversy for the Fellowship by not offering opinions on matters unrelated to CoDA. One way that we eliminate controversy for the group is not recommending outside sources, such as books or workshops. In CoDA, we use the Steps and Traditions of Co-Dependents Anonymous and CoDA Conference endorsed literature for guidance. This creates a safe environment for newcomers, ourselves, and CoDA as a whole.

When we gather together in CoDA, we place our common welfare first. Our personal recovery depends upon this commitment to CoDA's unity. We experience strength in our Fellowship when we keep the commitment to our common welfare. With our primary purpose foremost in our minds, we put aside our differences and welcome all those who desire healthy and loving relationships. We learn that an outside issue is anything that has the potential to distract us from our primary purpose as stated in Tradition Five, "Each group has but one primary purpose—to carry its message to other codependents who still suffer."

Tradition Ten also protects the spiritual nature of our program. We gather together to share our personal experience, strength, and hope of recovery from codependency. CoDA meetings are not the place to discuss our opinions about worldly topics. Honoring this Tradition, we provide a place of safety for everyone, regardless of religious or political preference. It does not matter who we are or what we do. It does matter that we work the Steps, follow the Traditions, and desire healthy and loving relationships.

CoDA has no opinion on outside issues; hence the CoDA name ought never be drawn into public controversy.

—Tradition Ten

These questions are intended to help you work Tradition Ten:

- What boundaries are established by this Tradition?

- What does "outside issue" mean to me?

- What does "public controversy" mean to me?

- How does this Tradition support the newcomer?

- How does Tradition Ten relate to Step Ten?

- How do I practice this Tradition?

- How does this Tradition protect the spiritual foundation of our program?

- If someone in my home group promotes a specific religious affiliation, is that a violation of Tradition Ten?

NOTES

NOTES

NOTES

NOTES

Sought through prayer and meditation to improve our conscious contact with God as we understood God, praying only for knowledge of God's will for us and the power to carry that out.

—Step Eleven

Step Eleven is an essential tool to use in our recovery from codependency. It reminds us that this program is an ongoing one, requiring daily maintenance. As we improve our conscious contact with God through prayer and meditation, we gain knowledge of God's will for us. We are asked to let go of our struggle to control and to turn to God, as we understand God, for our direction. This Step is one of our guides to developing more honest and loving relationships. Willing to improve our conscious contact, we humbly accept our journey of recovery.

Daily prayer and meditation connect us with the God of our understanding and how we want to live today. It is our way of acknowledging to ourselves that we are never alone. We can also let it be a time to humbly remember the character defects that have prevented us from recognizing God's will.

We approach prayer and meditation in many different ways. For many of us, this is not a formal event. Some commune with nature and the outdoors; some say words like "serenity" and "love" to feel quiet within; some use affirmations to bring their Higher Power into their thoughts; some kneel in quiet repose; some sit and breathe deeply; and some use self-talk to connect with themselves and their Higher Power. Prayer and meditation is our way of improving our conscious contact with the God of our understanding. It does not matter how we pray and meditate; what matters is that we do it.

This Step tells us to pray only for knowledge of God's will for us and the power to carry that out. We improve our conscious contact and increase awareness of our own reality, through prayer and meditation. We find the power we need to carry out God's will, as we work this Step.

Knowing we have a loving Higher Power, we find the strength and power to carry out God's will for us. Through prayer and meditation, we see connections between the events in our lives. We have come to believe there is a power greater than ourselves and are willing to turn our lives over to the care of God, as we understand God, as stated in Step Three. We are able to reflect on the wonder of our lives, with gratitude to our Higher Power.

Sought through prayer and meditation to improve our conscious contact with God as we understood God, praying only for knowledge of God's will for us and the power to carry that out.

—Step Eleven

These questions are intended to help you work Step Eleven:

- What helps me remember to use this Step?

- How do I use Step Eleven when I have a problem?

- How is my experience different as a result of working this Step?

- How do I use Step Eleven to support my recovery?

- How does praying for knowledge of God's will help simplify my life?

- What is prayer? How do I go about learning to pray?

- What is meditation? How do I go about learning to meditate?

- What is the God of my understanding today?

- What does improve my "conscious contact with God" mean to me?

- How do I know God's will for me? Do I trust myself to know God's will?

- How do I differentiate God's will from my will?

- What power do I have to carry out God's will for me?

- Why does this Step instruct us to pray "only for knowledge of God's will for us and the power to carry that out?"

NOTES

NOTES

NOTES

NOTES

Our public relations policy is based on attraction rather than promotion; we need always maintain personal anonymity at the level of press, radio, and films.

—Tradition Eleven

Tradition Eleven provides boundaries for the Fellowship and its individual members about how to interact with the public. Two guidelines are established. First, CoDA's "public relations policy is based on attraction rather than promotion." Second, as CoDA members, we each "maintain personal anonymity at the level of press, radio, and films."

What is attraction? Attraction is a force that draws things or people together. Every CoDA member practicing recovery has an inner quality that attracts others. We rely on this quality when we engage with the public concerning CoDA, instead of relying on outside publications or professionals. What are appropriate methods to attract new members? We make known the time and location of CoDA meetings without promising results, and we read and distribute CoDA's Conference endorsed literature.

Simply by living our program, attraction is possible. When others recognize our changes, our serenity, our honesty, we begin to hear questions such as, "How did you change?" or "What did you do?" If appropriate, we then share our personal experience, strength, and hope about how we live in recovery today and how that differs from the way we used to live. Honestly sharing our recovery with people attracts newcomers into the Fellowship.

Tradition Eleven asks us to avoid promotion. What is promotion? Promotion can be identifying ourselves professionally; offering opinions; and offering particular outcomes, such as suggesting that attending CoDA meetings will straighten out a marriage or that you'll feel better within a month. Another form of inappropriate promotion would be advertising that a prominent author recommends Co-Dependents Anonymous or advertising that goes beyond simply informing the public about meetings.

Another aspect of this Tradition speaks to anonymity. Anonymous means unidentified or undeclared. Personal anonymity supports a boundary for each CoDA member to stay unidentified at the public relations level. When all in recovery maintain personal anonymity, we find the CoDA unity we need for personal recovery. We rely on living our individual programs. CoDA has no hierarchy; therefore, no one person speaks for CoDA as a whole.

Why do we have a public relations policy? "Each group has but one primary purpose—to carry its message to other codependents who still suffer," according to the Fifth Tradition. Furthermore, Step Twelve tells us "to carry this message to other codependents and to practice these principles in all our affairs." In order for us to carry out our purpose, we provide meeting information and CoDA literature. We offer our experience, strength, and hope and leave the rest to our Higher Power.

Our public relations policy is based on attraction rather than promotion; we need always maintain personal anonymity at the level of press, radio, and films.

—Tradition Eleven

These questions are intended to help you work Tradition Eleven:

- What does "attraction rather than promotion" mean to me? How is attraction different from promotion?

- What is our public relations policy?

- What does maintaining personal anonymity at the level of press, radio, and films mean to me?

- Why do I think it's important to maintain personal anonymity in our public relations? How do I do that?

- How does this Tradition support the spiritual and humble nature of our program?

- How do I apply this Tradition when I'm talking about my experience with someone outside the program?

- What codependent feelings and/or issues come up for me as I work this Tradition?

- How does the first part of this Tradition relate to the second part of this Tradition?

- How does breaking anonymity harm CoDA?

- How does my home meeting attract and/or welcome newcomers?

NOTES

NOTES

NOTES

NOTES

Having had a spiritual awakening as the result of these steps, we tried to carry this message to other codependents and to practice these principles in all our affairs.

—Step Twelve

Step Twelve tells us that the result of working the Steps is a spiritual awakening. A spiritual awakening could be described as the way members find their Higher Power and what each member has received from working the Twelve Steps. There will be a transformation; we will see and understand ourselves differently. One member shared her awakening as, "The same events are happening as before. It's my experience of the events that is different." Another member shared, "My spiritual awakening is that I have the Steps of CoDA and my Higher Power" and yet another shared, "My spiritual awakening is that I am a spiritual human being." Sharing about our spiritual awakenings in meetings is one way we can carry the message and bring hope to codependents. We hear how the Steps worked for others and that helps us to have faith that the Steps can work for us.

Sometimes spiritual awakenings are gradual and experienced through hindsight, like coming to the realization that we are the ones who need to change and we cannot change others. We are reminded that our spiritual awakening is a result and comes after the time has been spent working the Steps. We are capable of changing by using tools we have found from working the Steps. Some of those tools are taking inventory, making amends, using a daily Tenth Step, meditating, and praying. As a member shared, "I have spiritual awakenings all the time, each time I go from a place of codependency to a place of God's will." Continuing to work the Steps helps sustain our spiritual awakenings. We come to believe that God is within us and not separate from us.

Step Twelve gives us a directive as members. We try to carry the message of our spiritual awakening to other codependents. The word "try" implies that we make the effort and let go of the results. Gradually, we come to understand that our recovery is the message. Having worked through the Twelve Steps, we are different; our lives have changed. Therefore, simply living our lives of recovery is important. We don't always know when someone suffering is listening to or noticing us. Humbly sharing our experiences of recovery in meetings secures our own recovery and, at the same time, carries the message of recovery. As members of CoDA, there are other ways we try to carry the message. Some examples are bringing meetings to those who are confined in hospitals, prisons, or other institutions; sponsoring a new member; speaking; and doing service at all levels of CoDA. It is important to have CoDA's literature available to carry our message of recovery to newcomers and those still suffering.

This Step suggests that the principles of our program can be applied to all aspects of our lives. Learning to live life differently, we become aware that we cannot separate our recovery from other aspects of our lives. After all, codependency affected all areas of our lives, so we want to apply our knowledge of the Twelve Steps in all those areas. These principles of our program are the road map to a more sane way of living. They help us see ourselves and what we are doing or not doing. We no longer have to feel crazy and confused without a place to go. We have the Twelve Steps and our Higher Power to help us make wise decisions. Continuing to practice these principles, we experience life in a different way and carry this message to other codependents.

Having had a spiritual awakening as the result of these steps, we tried to carry this message to other codependents and to practice these principles in all our affairs.

—Step Twelve

These questions are intended to help you work Step Twelve:

• Have I had a spiritual awakening as the result of working these Steps?

• How do I know if I've had a spiritual awakening?

• How is the hope of our program conveyed in this Step?

• What is my experience in trying to carry the message?

• What tools do I have today as a result of the Steps?

• How does my spiritual awakening affect my life?

• What might separate me from my spiritual awakening or Higher Power?

• What are "these principles" referred to in the Twelfth Step?

• How do I practice these principles in all my affairs?

NOTES

NOTES

NOTES

NOTES

Anonymity is the spiritual foundation of all our Traditions,
ever reminding us to place principles before personalities.

— Tradition Twelve

Tradition Twelve clarifies that CoDA is a spiritual program and that "anonymity is the spiritual foundation of all our Traditions." Further, anonymity is the base for us to operate from in our meetings and groups, thereby placing "principles before personalities." Doing this protects our program. Simply stated, without anonymity CoDA's structure will fall apart.

In Tradition Eleven, we talked about the meaning of maintaining anonymity in our public relations policy. Now, in Tradition Twelve, we look at coming together in our meetings and CoDA service work with the spirit of anonymity. Being anonymous may include not only keeping our last names private, but also where we live, how much money we make, and what we do for a living. This reduces the possibility of personally judging others and ourselves. Because social, economic, and political differences are not identified within the Fellowship, every member can focus on recovery from codependency. We have the unique opportunity to listen and work with people who have the same goal. With the boundary of anonymity, we are reminded that we come together for one primary purpose: to carry the message of recovery to codependents who still suffer.

Anonymity creates safety because it establishes an environment where we can speak with less fear of being judged or quoted. As one member shared, "I've had the painful experience of being judged by others. Now, in my program, I can make a choice not to behave in that same judgmental way. I remember that everyone is entitled to his or her own opinion. When I listen, consider, and accept, then I know I have heard the principle of what was said." When we honor the concept of anonymity, we place "principles before personalities." Thus, we listen to what is said, not who is saying it. We don't bring our personal agendas to CoDA; we bring our concern of recovery from codependency. "Spiritual" is not defined within our program. Therefore, each member's path or belief is welcome; CoDA is completely inclusive.

Tradition Twelve teaches us to adhere to all of our Traditions by placing the principles of our Traditions before personalities. When we keep this principle first and foremost, CoDA can maintain a healthy existence. The Traditions teach each member and group of Co-Dependents Anonymous how to protect our anonymous, spiritual, and inclusive Fellowship.

Anonymity is the spiritual foundation of all our Traditions,
ever reminding us to place principles before personalities.

— Tradition Twelve

These questions are intended to help you work Tradition Twelve:

- What does "anonymity" mean to me?

- How does anonymity create a spiritual foundation for our Traditions?

- What does anonymity mean to a CoDA group?

- Why is it important for the group to uphold anonymity?

- What does "place principles before personalities" mean to me?

- How does anonymity help me to place principles before personalities?

- How do I practice the principle of anonymity for myself? Others?

- How does Tradition Twelve keep my meeting safe?

- How does this Tradition protect our program?

NOTES

NOTES

NOTES

NOTES

Traditions Checklist for Group Inventory

When we have questions or problems in CoDA, we can use a checklist of all Twelve Traditions to find the answers to our questions or the causes of the problem. Using the Traditions in this manner provides every group with a way to do a group inventory.

We can ask ourselves questions such as:

- Does our common welfare come first as we do service work?

- Do we rely on our loving Higher Power, as expressed through our group conscience, for our ultimate authority?

- Do we remember that the only requirement for membership in CoDA is a desire for healthy and loving relationships?

- Do we honor each group's autonomy except in matters affecting other groups or CoDA as a whole?

- Do we remember that each group's primary purpose is to carry the message of recovery to other codependents who still suffer?

- Do we avoid endorsing outside enterprises and therefore not divert ourselves from our primary spiritual aim?

- Are we self-supporting?

- Do we remain nonprofessional in our service?

- Are we directly responsible to those we serve?

- Do we remember that CoDA has no opinion on outside issues, to avoid drawing CoDA into public controversy?

- Do we base our public relations policy on attraction rather than promotion?

- Are we honoring the principle of anonymity?

These more personalized questions may assist in your recovery process.

- What positive characteristics do I have? What are my best qualities? What are my talents? What successes am I most proud of?

- As a child, was anyone there to talk with or otherwise support me? What conclusions have I drawn about this?

- As a child, did I experience codependent behaviors from my caregivers? How did I feel about these behaviors at the time? What conclusions or beliefs have I drawn from these behaviors? How do I feel about them now?

- Do I feel I deserve good things? If not, why?

- What positive experiences were parts of my childhood? What did I gain from these experiences? What positive messages were given to me in childhood? Who or what was the source of these messages? How did they make me feel?

- Do I deny my parents' codependency or addiction? If so, why? What do I get from denial? Am I able to accept that my parents did what they did because it is how they were, rather than blaming them or myself?

- What things am I doing (repeating) today that were done to me as a child? What self-defeating behaviors have I carried into my adult life from my family of origin? In what places other than my family did I learn these?

- What do I love about myself?

- How have I, as an adult, caused harm to myself?

- Do I criticize and condemn myself and others? Under what circumstances?

- How do I allow other people's opinions to influence my behavior? Why?

- What values of mine do I ignore in order to fit in?

- Do I tend to discount myself? Where did I learn this? How does this make me feel?

- Do I place more importance on what others think than what I think? If yes, why?

- As an adult, what is my payoff in believing I am a victim? Give examples.

- What codependent behaviors am I holding on to? What am I accomplishing or trying to cover up with my codependent behaviors?

- Do I believe others' behaviors are my fault or responsibility? What learning experiences have I denied others in my efforts to control them?

- Give examples of when I took on more responsibility than I needed to, or thought I was in charge, but wasn't? What was the outcome?

- What resentments am I holding on to? How do the resentments affect my recovery? What am I avoiding? Why?

- Has anyone ever said, "What's the matter with you? Stop that right now!" or otherwise negated my feelings? How did this make me feel?

- When have I owned my power? How did it feel?

- How has my recovery benefited me?

NOTES

NOTES

NOTES

NOTES

NOTES

NOTES

NOTES

PREAMBLE©
The Co-Dependents Anonymous
Program of Recovery

Co-Dependents Anonymous is a Fellowship of men and women whose common purpose is to develop healthy relationships. The only requirement for membership is a desire for healthy and loving relationships. We gather together to support and share with each other in a journey of self-discovery – learning to love the self. Living the program allows each of us to become increasingly honest with ourselves about our personal histories and our own codependent behaviors.

We rely upon the Twelve Steps and Twelve Traditions for knowledge and wisdom. These are the principles of our program and guides to developing honest and fulfilling relationships with ourselves and others. In CoDA, we each learn to build a bridge to a Higher Power of our own understanding, and we allow others the same privilege.

This renewal process is a gift of healing for us. By actively working the program of Co-Dependents Anonymous, we can each realize a new joy, acceptance, and serenity in our lives.

WELCOME©

We welcome you to Co-Dependents Anonymous, a program of recovery from codependence, where each of us may share our experience, strength, and hope in our efforts to find freedom where there has been bondage, and peace where there has been turmoil in our relationships with others and ourselves.

Most of us have been searching for ways to overcome the dilemmas of the conflicts in our relationships and our childhoods. Many of us were raised in families where addictions existed – some of us were not. In either case, we have found in each of our lives that codependence is a most deeply-rooted, compulsive behavior, and that it is born out of our sometimes moderately, sometimes extremely dysfunctional family systems.

We have each experienced in our own ways the painful trauma of the emptiness of our childhood and relationships throughout our lives. We attempted to use others–our mates, our friends, and even our children–as our sole source of identity, value, and well-being, and as a way of trying to restore within us the emotional losses from our childhoods. Our histories may include other powerful addictions which at times we have used to cope with our codependence.

We have all learned to survive life, but in CoDA we are learning to live life. Through applying the Twelve Steps and principles found in CoDA to our daily life and relationships, both present and past, we can experience a new freedom from our self-defeating lifestyles. It is an individual growth process. Each of us is growing at our own pace and will continue to do so as we remain open to God's will for us on a daily basis. Our sharing is our way of identification and helps us to free the emotional bonds of our past and the compulsive control of our present.

No matter how traumatic your past or despairing your present may seem, there is hope for a new day in the program of Co-Dependents Anonymous. No longer do you need to rely on others as a power greater than yourself. May you instead find here a new strength within to be that which God intended – Precious and Free.

CoDA Opening Prayer ©
In the spirit of love and truth,
we ask our Higher Power
to guide us as we share
our experience, strength, and hope.
We open our hearts to the light of wisdom,
the warmth of love, and the joy of acceptance.

CoDA Closing Prayer ©
We thank our Higher Power
for all that we have received from this meeting.
As we close, may we take with us
the wisdom, love, acceptance,
and hope of recovery.

COPYRIGHT ASSIGNMENT

THIS ASSIGNMENT ("Assignment") is made by and between Co-Dependents Anonymous, Inc., an Arizona corporation with offices located at P.O. Box 33577, Phoenix, AZ 85067 ("CoDA"), and _____ ("Assignor").

Assignor is the sole owner of an undivided whole interest in the literary work(s) of authorship entitled: _____ (the "Copyrights"), including all rights throughout the world, and warrants that he or she was born in the year _____ and is a citizen of or domiciled in _____; and CoDA desires to acquire an undivided whole interest in the Assignor's right, title and interest in the Copyrights;

NOW, THEREFORE, for consideration publication of the Copyrights, the adequacy of which is hereby acknowledged, Assignor hereby sells, assigns, and transfers to CoDA, its legal representatives, successors and assigns, all of Assignor's right, title and interest in and to the Copyrights, as well as any registrations and copyright registration applications relating thereto, along with the right to secure renewals, reissues, and extensions of the Copyrights; all works based upon, derived from, or incorporating the Work; all income, royalties, damages, claims and payments now or hereafter due or payable with respect thereto; all causes of action, either in law or in equity for past, present, or future infringement based on the copyrights; and all rights corresponding to the foregoing throughout the world. Without additional consideration, Assignor agrees to execute all papers and to perform such other proper acts as CoDA may deem necessary to secure for CoDA or its designee the rights assigned herein. Assignor agrees that any dispute between Assignor and CoDA relating to the Copyrights and which cannot be resolved amicably will be resolved by binding arbitration under the then-current commercial arbitration rules of the American Arbitration Association in Phoenix, Arizona, or at such other location as the CoDA Board of Directors may reasonably select.

Executed this _____ day of _____, 20____ at _____
(City and State)

By: _____

Print Name: _____
(Full Legal Name)

Address: _____

_____

_____